The Practice of Group Therapy

THE PRACTICE OF
GROUP THERAPY

S. R. Slavson, Editor

Foreword

by

Nolan D. C. Lewis, M. D.

INTERNATIONAL UNIVERSITIES PRESS

New York   New York

CONTENTS

CONTENTS

LIST OF AUTHORS

ACKERMAN, NATHAN W., M. D., Member, Faculty of the Psychoanalytic Clinic for Training and Research, Columbia University; Director, Council Child Development Center, New York; Secretary, Association for Psychoanalytic Medicine; Lecturer, New York School for Social Work.

BARUCH, DOROTHY W., Ph. D., Consultant Psychologist, Los Angeles, California.

GABRIEL, BETTY, Senior Psychiatric Caseworker, Child Guidance Institute, Jewish Board of Guardians, New York; Psychiatric Consultant, East Bronx Community Y.

GLATZER, HENRIETTE T., Psychotherapist, Guidance Center of New Rochelle, New York.

GREENE, JAMES SONNETT, M. D., Director, National Hospital of Speech Disorders, New York; Consultant on Speech and Voice Disorders, Memorial Hospital, and New York Eye and Ear Infirmary, New York.

HOLLAND, GEORGE, Senior Group Therapist, Child Guidance Institute, Jewish Board of Guardians, New York.

KLAPMAN, J. W., M. D., Member, Faculty Northwestern Medical School, Chicago; Staff Member, Institute for Juvenile Research, Chicago.

LEWIS, NOLAN D. C., M. D., Director, New York State Psychiatric Institute; Professor of Psychiatry, Columbia University.

LISTER, LOUIS, Senior Group Therapist, Jewish Board of Guardians, New York.

7

MILLER, HYMAN, M. D., Associate Attending Physician, Cedars of Lebanon Hospital, Los Angeles, California; Senior Attending Physician and Chief of the Allergy Clinic and Hospital, Allergy Service, Los Angeles General Hospital, Los Angeles, California; Consultant in Allergy, U. S. Veterans Administration Sawtelle Hospital, Sawtelle, California; Associate Clinical Professor of Medicine, University of Southern California Medical School, Los Angeles, California.

PEDERSON-KRAG, GERALDINE, M. D., Member, Royal College of Surgeons of England; Licentiate, Royal College of Physicians, London, England.

SCHEIDLINGER, SAUL, Assistant to the Director of Group Therapy, Jewish Board of Guardians, New York.

SCHIFFER, MORTIMER, Board of Education Liaison Representative, Children's Court, New York City; Senior Group Therapist, Jewish Board of Guardians, New York.

SIEGEL, MIRIAM, Ph. D., Psychologist, Council Child Development Center, New York.

SLAVSON, S. R., Director of Group Therapy, Jewish Board of Guardians, New York; Consultant in Group Therapy: Community Service Society, New York; Bridgeport Mental Hygiene Society, Bridgeport, Connecticut; Jewish Child Guidance Bureau, Newark, N. J.; Council Child Development Center, New York. Past President, American Group Therapy Association.

SPOTNITZ, HYMAN, M. D., D. Med. Sc., Psychiatrist, Jewish Board of Guardians, New York; Assistant Neurologist, Neurological Institute, New York; Assistant Neurologist, Vanderbilt Clinic, New York.

VAN OPHUIJSEN, J. H. W., M. D., Member, Teaching Staff, New York Psychoanalytic Institute; Attending in Psychiatry, Veterans Hospital, Bronx, New York; Chief Consulting Psychiatrist, Jewish Board of Guardians, New York.

FOREWORD

The increasing interest in Group Psychotherapy is ample evidence of the serious attempts that are being made to supply aid to a vast number of people in need of support and guidance in solving of their various emotional and social problems. The urgent need for psychotherapy is acknowledged and emphasized everywhere in modern psychiatric literature. Almost every issue of the military and civilian medical journals comment on the desirability of additional psychotherapy and psychotherapists.

Group Psychotherapy is basically a special application of the principles of individual treatment to two or more persons simultaneously, which brings also into the situation the phenomena and problems of interpersonal relationships.

Curative therapy depends both upon the etiology and status of the disorder, and the concepts and type of procedure utilized by the therapist.

The underlying aim of Group Therapy is to introduce therapeutic activity designed to direct the individual's efforts toward useful undertakings and to clarify the psychological conflicts that they may be transformed into a normal way of living. Sufficient knowledge of the problem to allow a judicious application of the right therapy at the right time is the ideal toward which all psychiatrists strive throughout their professional lives.

It is frequently stated, and sometimes as a criticism, that Group Therapy may be anxiety producing. This is probably true, but it does not follow necessarily that the anxiety is an undesirable reaction, as it may bring into the open certain matters that can be relieved by the group contacts. The patient may then experience anxiety reduction that restores self-confidence which enables him to adjust more comfortably to previously annoying symptoms. Mobilized anxiety, if not too severe and "explosive," may be utilized to advantage therapeutically.

9

It creates the ability in some patients to detect the fallacies in evasive practices and mechanisms utilized by others in the group, and aids them in maintaining any newly acquired corrective attitudes in the presence of active opposition on the part of others less informed or not yet able to accept a more workable life plan.

Experts in Group Therapy do not claim that it is a substitute for individual treatment, but feel that it is indicated in special, carefully chosen cases, with a proper assignment as far as the composition of the group is concerned. No one type of group treatment is suitable for all patients, as various kinds of activity are required in keeping with the presenting symptoms and needs.

As in any other kind of therapeutic endeavor, the one doing the job, i. e. the therapist, is of particular importance and the degree of his success will be determined by a number of factors among which are the solidity as well as the flexibility of his own personality integration, suitability of temperament, capacity for understanding others, empathic index, knowledge of the complexities of behavior, and his training and experience in the specialty.

It is apparent that Group Therapy is on its way to receive a wide application and thus a thorough trial. For this reason it is important to have reliable sources of information for those entering the field, as well as for those who desire to learn about techniques, selection of patients, limitations, qualifications, and other pertinent matters. This book, *The Practice of Group Therapy*, organized by S. R. Slavson, who with his co-workers and collaborators, has furnished such an authoritative text for all students interested in the subject, is needed and timely.

The authors of this book have covered the areas of their choice with careful consideration and with an appreciation of the complexity of the subject. A wide sweep of topics ranging from general principles, dynamics, and techniques of Group Therapy, to its outlook for the future have been presented by workers among whom there are those who have described their particular experiences in chapters dealing with the problems of children, of the psychoneurotic and psychotic, of the psychopathic personality, and with some attention to psychosomatic disturbances. The special case studies will be of particular interest to those who desire to follow the details of the involved relationships and factors in the process.

This informative contribution in a field that is not well understood as yet, should be very helpful to all concerned with the correction of personal and interpersonal psychological disturbances.

NOLAN D. C. LEWIS

EDITOR'S PREFACE

This book is intended to describe specifically the application of various types of Group Therapy to emotionally disturbed, socially maladjusted, and mental patients as they are found in the general practice of psychiatry and psychotherapy. Part I deals with the general consideration of Group Therapy, Part II with a special type evolved in the last decade and a half, known as Activity Group Therapy, and Part III is devoted to a form of psychotherapy that has been employed for a much longer period of time, which we designate as Interview Group Therapy. The latter is sometimes referred to as Discussion Therapy. A chapter on Didactic Group Psychotherapy with psychotic patients is also included.

It has been the aim of the editor of this book to relate treatment to specific clinical categories and diagnostic entities as they are employed in the general practice of psychiatry. In the actual practice such specificity is frequently not possible to achieve, and the reader will find that the contributors of Chapters Eight and Nine use symptomatology in grouping patients. This was inevitable because the authors, as practitioners, were specialists in a given field.

While the use of Group Therapy for the treatment of patients with special symptoms, as differentiated from psychological syndromes, may have certain weaknesses, those who have been concerned with personality problems in special areas found it necessary to address themselves to the symptom-problem involved. However, it would seem that there is considerable validity in adhering to the rule of employing Group Therapy to patients with the same syndromes rather than symptoms.

One of the features of this book is that it represents the cooperative effort of medical and non-medical psychotherapists:

psychiatrists, psychiatric caseworkers, group therapists, and psychologists. Particularly is Chapter Ten important in this respect. The full psychiatric team cooperated in the case reported in this chapter, namely, the caseworker, psychiatrist, psychologist and group therapist.

While the book is a cooperative venture on the part of a number of persons, the chapters do not stand as separate contributions. They have been integrated into a unit-whole, which might be in effect the product of one author. To accomplish this, it was necessary to enlist the willingness of the contributors to follow the same outline and plan in the writing of all the chapters. The editor has undertaken the responsibility of eliminating as far as possible repetitions of general principles, which makes this book a unit. Despite this, the opinions of each author and his specific contribution to the total treatise were carefully preserved. In order to get this unity it was necessary to ask the authors to revise their contributions, sometimes more than once, and in some instances conferences were held with them.

The editor wishes to express his deep appreciation of the contributors' forebearance and tolerance with which they have considered his suggestions. It is only in the spirit of such cooperativeness that a work such as this is made possible. In a real sense this book is an experiment in cooperative-coordinative writing.

The reader's special attention is called to Chapters Six, Seven, Ten, and Eleven dealing with the actual treatment of cases. These are the longest, but in view of the intention of this volume are of particular importance. These chapters were written with a view of demonstrating the *actual process*. Chapter Eleven on Relationship Therapy demonstrates more than any other the concept of treatment *in a group* to which reference is made in Chapter Nine, page 178, as against *treatment through a group*. The therapist describes how she worked through the problems of one individual patient in the presence of the group. As a contrast to that is treatment *through the group* as demonstrated by Chapter Six. In the latter the description of the therapeutic process is directed toward a particular child, actually the entire group was involved with all the other members participating.

All of the chapters except One, Two and Three are based on papers presented at the conferences of the American Group Therapy Association in the years of 1945-47. The others were especially written for the purpose of giving a fuller presentation of the application of Group Therapy to various psychological problems. This volume has been prepared at the initiative of the American Group Therapy Association, and it wishes to express its unqualifying gratitude to the International Universities Press, Inc., for making it available to psychotherapists. The editor wishes to express his deep gratitude to Dr. Gertrud M. Kurth, who worked diligently and enthusiastically during the preparation of this volume for publication. He also wishes to express his appreciation of Dr. J. H. W. van Ophuijsen and Dr. Nolan D. C. Lewis for their contributions.

S. R. S.

New York,
August 28, 1947

PART I
GENERAL PRINCIPLES

Chapter One

GENERAL PRINCIPLES AND DYNAMICS

The recognition in recent years of the difference between child psychiatry and adult psychiatry has been one of the significant developments in psychotherapy. The child's ego is in many respects different from that of the adult. It is still in the process of evolving, and the balance between primitive impulses and restraint has not been established as in the case with the average adult. Whether impulses or the restraining forces predominate, each person has worked out a relation between the two, which is the foundation of his character. In some, behavior is more dominated by impulses, in others, primitive drives and spontaneity are under control, and those we consider the more mature. Whatever the resolution of these two opposite psychic forces, impulse and their control, a state of balance is achieved for the particular individual. This is not the situation with the young child.

He is still in the process of formation in relation to both the outer world and to the many drives within himself. He is still working out some pattern for his life, and is moving toward a state of comparative equilibrium that will be eventually established. The child's emotions are labile and his behavior inconsistent. He is experimenting with himself and with life. There is considerable swing of moods, transilience, and shorter periods of concentration. Such fluidity is mostly a result of his still unstable organic balance due to growth. Emotionally, too, he is more variable and pliable than a grownup. His social awareness and his superego are not as yet rigid. His capacity to identify is greater and objects of identification change frequently. First, there are the parents; then come various relatives, playmates, teachers, heroes, and fictional characters. Friendships are not permanent and become more or less fixed later. Thus the operational field of a child tends to be less restricted than that of an adult and his capacity for change and re-integration is much greater.

The child seeks to protect himself against frustration of his primitive impulses. He is resentful of restraint and, because of his instability, is given readily to rage and anger when inhibited. While the average adult is defending himself against injury to his superego—the sense of right and wrong and community judgments of himself—the child is not so much concerned with these. His greater concern is freedom of locomotion, action and expression. He has an impelling need to play, to be aggressive and self-indulgent. These two contrasting drives have been described as "id resistances" on the part of the child and "superego resistances" on the part of the adult. In this state of flux and change, the child is following the pressures of organic forces and the forces of his psychic life. He is a growing, evolving organism with concomitant psychological drives, but much of the child's needs are also derived from the dynamic processes inherent in biological growth.

Growth increases potential energy which has to be transformed into kinetic energy, or activity. This relation between potential and kinetic energy is not restricted to man; it is present in inanimate nature as the potential energy in chemicals, in electricity, as well as in all organic life. Thus restriction and inhibition that do not follow the laws of orderly development of the total personality produce psychic tension in the same way as destructive emotional relations do. When a child is frustrated there occurs a concomitant feeling of rejection. But as Freud has pointed out, psychologic tensions may originate in the organism and organic disturbances can have their roots in emotional stress. Libido travels a two-way path: from the soma to the psyche and vice versa.

In addition to the id and superego defenses, there are also the "ego defenses," namely the protection one builds up in order to maintain a sense of self-esteem, a feeling of power and status.

These ego defenses are very strong, both in children and in adults, and must be considered in the picture of the total personality.

The young child's unconscious is also comparatively near the surface. Primary impulses are not under control; repressions and inhibitions have not been established and the superego not yet fully evolved. The young child tends to speak his mind, as it were, acts out his negative impulses and is demonstrative in his affections. On the whole, it may be said that since repressions are not yet operating adequately, his unconscious and conscious are in close proximity, if not in a hopeless tangle which is unravelled and reorganized only later in life. It is for this reason that restraint of the young child's behavior in the treatment situation is so important, as has been suggested elsewhere.[1] He still has to evolve inner controls and selective judgment, which he does through identification with specific adults and through incorporating their attitudes and values into the structure of his own psyche. This is not the case with older children and adolescents, where the differentiation between the impulses and their control has been established and the ego structure achieved.

Science and scientific practice usually develop from the general to the particular. The inductive method leads to generalizations and formulations that, when applied, require further breakdown to suit specific situations. This order in the evolution of a science is true of psychotherapy as well. The general formulations of the nature of mental and emotional disorders were first applied in blanket fashion. Hypnotism and suggestion have had their day,[2] and descriptive psychiatry has undergone important changes in recent years. Nomenclature, classifications and diagnoses which constituted the systematic psychiatry of only a few decades ago, have given way to a dynamic, therapeutic psy-

[1] Slavson, S. R.: Differential Methods of Group Therapy in Relation to Age Levels, *Nerv. Child*, April, 1945.

[2] Hypnotism needs to be differentiated from hypnotherapy or hypnoanalysis where the hypnotic or post-hypnotic trance are employed only as a means for reducing resistance. In the latter the actual therapy is not achieved by hypnosis, but through the psychotherapeutic interview in, or following hypnosis.

chiatry. Emphasis is laid upon skills and methods of treatment rather than upon classification and description. Freud's contributions are the motive-force behind this very important change; but psychoanalysts, as well, have found it necessary to re-adapt their practice to meet the treatment needs of specific clients.

Modern psychotherapy, having left the realm of magic and suggestion, takes in consideration the total personality of people with whom it deals. This is true not only of psychotherapy, but of education and medicine as well.[3] Educators and recreationists are becoming increasingly aware of the need to evaluate their work in terms of its effect upon the *total* personality of pupils or participants. They are rapidly leaving behind the limitations of specialties, such as physical health and intellectual development, and are moving to an increasing degree into the field of mental hygiene. As could be expected, psychiatrists, psychotherapists and social workers, especially psychiatric caseworkers, have made the greatest progress in this direction. This can be considered as one of the major developments both in corrective and educational efforts today, and in psychiatry's increased service to the community.

Many significant contributions, though varying in essential details from the original source, have been derived from the teachings of Freud. Ego therapy, relationship therapy, insight therapy, release therapy and the many other techniques—all stem from the parent trunk of psychoanalysis. This is equally true of Group Therapy, which is one of the most recent developments. One cannot assume that all persons who come for help with problems in personal and social adjustment can, or should be, treated in groups; but it is our understanding, based upon years of observation and experimentation, that a large number of persons, and especially children can be helped through groups only. In fact, the younger the child is, the more suitable is Group Therapy for him unless there are specific counter-indications, some of which are dealt with in this volume, in Chapter Five.

It is clear that no one method of therapy can be regarded as universally applicable. The effectiveness of a method of treat-

[3] See Chapter Eight.

ment, with its variations, rests upon its suitable application to a particular patient. Frequently, it is necessary to combine several methods. Perhaps the greatest skill of a therapist lies in his ability to understand the patient's nuclear problem, to gain insight into the dynamics of his character and personality—often through intuitive perception—and to select the line of treatment to which the patient will best respond. When the patient and treatment are matched, we can expect successful outcome, and certainly more rapid results than in cases where treatment procedures are rigidly imposed.

We have seen that this approach is not only rational, but is used in all enlightened efforts. Workers in education, recreation, social work, therapy and industry—in fact, in all fields that involve human relations—find that individualization is the primary condition for success. Blanket techniques are being systematically abandoned for the more effective and more realistic methods of individualization. Thus, flexibility is a prime condition for successful work with people and it is also a prime condition for success in psychotherapy. Awareness of this has resulted in many new developments in psychotherapy in recent years, one of which is Group Therapy. As Group Therapy was employed with a variety of patients and clients, it, too, had to be modified to meet the needs of individual cases.[4]

It is the particular aim of this book to indicate its applicability and to describe, in a practical manner, the way Group Therapy can be used in specific cases. Prevalent clinical categories are used as a base to show how the various types of therapy groups can be used. In practice, and this is especially true of hospitals and other institutions, it may sometimes be necessary to group patients in accordance with some gross symptom. The use to which Group Therapy has been put in such instances is described in Chapters Eight and Nine.

The chief and common value of the group is that it permits *acting out* of instinctual drives, which is accelerated by the catalytic effect of the other members. There is less caution and greater abandon in a group where the members find support in

[4] Slavson, S. R., Current Practices in Group Therapy. *Ment. Hygiene.* July, 1944.

one another and the fear of self-revelation is strikingly reduced.
As a result, patients reveal their problems more easily, and therapy is speeded up. Defenses are diminished, the permissiveness
of the total environment and the example set by others allow
each to let go with decreased self-protective restraint. Although
groups lessen the defenses of adults as well, this is particularly
true of children and adolescents. Free acting out and talking
through yield satisfaction. At the same time it brings patients
face to face with their problems quite early in treatment. The
defenses against injury to one's self-esteem are also reduced.[5]
The friendly group climate and the mutual acceptance do not
require one to be on the defensive. All have the same or similar
problems and no negative reactions are anticipated by anyone.
Status is assured. There is no fear of retaliation or debasement.

But release and abreaction alone are not enough. Therapy
must find means to re-integrate the personality, re-shape attitudes
and give the patient means for dealing with his life in new ways.
Each chapter in this book is designed to describe how this is
achieved through Group Therapy with patients of a specific
type.

If one were to read with care the writings of the ancients,
one would hardly fail to find reference to the group as a vehicle
for spiritual uplift and an antidote to mental depression. But we
need not go so far back to find value in group association for the
development of the human personality and the correction of the
many deviations to which man is subject. The phenomenon of
grouping is ever present all around us. It is evident in various
forms in nature, such as colonies of cells, droves of insects, flocks
of birds, schools of fish, herds of mammals, and groups among
men. The "collective instinct" is a biological device for survival
and it is a compelling need in living tissue, organisms and to
some extent, also in inanimate matter. When we deal with
groups, we deal with the very essence of life and the persistent
oversight of group attitudes and group pressures in education

---

[5] We referred to this as "ego-defenses," see p. 20.

and therapy has retarded our understanding of man and his motives.

Recently, the question was asked by a writer: "Is the group a natural phenomenon or is it man-made?" The notion that a group is a device orginated by man to achieve specific ends is disproved by the facts of nature and of life. All life manifests itself in some form of grouping. Certainly among living organisms, the fact strikes us inescapably that there is no life without a group. Fabre has written a number of fascinating books on the social life of insects; Maeterlinck wrote his famous work on *The Life of the Bee*, and more recently, Professor Allee of Chicago University published a very compelling book entitled *The Social Life of Animals*. The latter is based upon hundreds of experiments in and out of laboratories in many countries, which show that the proximity of animals to one another, within certain densities, is not only universal but also beneficial. In fact, in some instances, it is crucial in their existence.

Peter Kropotkin's famous work, *Mutual Aid as a Factor in Evolution* disproved the universality of Darwin's claim of the *struggle for existence*. What keeps animals alive is their mutual aid. He describes instances where horses when attacked by wolves, arrange themselves in a circle with their heads inward, kicking at the wolves at whatever point they attempt to attack until the wolves become exhausted and leave. Conversely, horned animals form circles with their heads outward and protect themselves in that way.

Only recently psychopathologists have recognized the group foundations of personality and of mental disturbances. Among the modern pioneers in this field is Trigand Burrow who called attention to it some decades ago. Freud also discussed it in his volume on *Group Psychology and the Analysis of the Ego*.

However, in recent years, acceptance of these principles has come from a field other than psychiatry and psychotherapy. *Group workers*, persons who work with people in groups in recreation and leisure time occupations, have greatly stimulated both sociologists and psychologists to the appreciation of the im-

portance of the group in determining and correcting human behavior. Perhaps their greatest service lay not so much in the
scientific discoveries or formulations of dynamics. Their work
rather served to call attention to the inter-action of the individual
and the group. The understanding of actual dynamics of multiple relations in group living will probably emerge from the study
of group pathology as has been the case in other sciences dealing
with man.

In terms of therapy, groups have many advantages. Whether in
Activity Group Therapy, Group Play (Play-Interview) Therapy,
or Interview Group Therapy,[6] groups help the therapeutic process. Release and catharsis occur much more easily and intensively
than is usual in any other treatment situation. The ego defenses
are reduced, and as Freud pointed out, the primitive impulses
flow more easily in groups than they do in individual relationships. Transference is greatly facilitated because the group is a
protection against the therapist and what he stands for: a symbol
of parental and environmental authority. At the same time, however, transference at times becomes greatly intensified, particularly its negative phases. There is reinforcement of the hostile
trends against the therapist, which makes his role rather difficult. But because of this very fact, and the opportunity for
acting out, therapy is accelerated. Transference in groups is also
intensified on its positive levels when there is sibling rivalry and
the patients make a bid for the love of the therapist.

Many patients are unable to make an adjustment to an ordinary
group of persons, either organized or unorganized, because it is
one of *social fixity*. In such a group, the individual must adjust
to a predetermined pattern, where demands are made upon him,
and where he must needs meet these demands in order to be
accepted. The effort to do this, and the ensuing restraints and
modifications in personality may cause him to withdraw from
fixed groups. A therapy group is one of *social mobility* [7] in which
he is able to fit because he is permitted to act out freely, to dis-

[6] Current Practices in Group Therapy, *loc. cit.*

[7] Slavson, S. R.: Some Elements in Activity Group Therapy, *Amer. J.
Orthopsych.* October, 1944.

charge his feelings and to display his attitudes; nor is he expected to modify his actions or language.

Recently, such phrases as "group formation," "group emotion," and "group symptom," have found their way into the literature on Group Therapy. While such terms arrest attention, they actually do not apply to treatment groups. In fact, the greatest single therapeutic value of such groups is the very absence of group formation. There is compresence, inter-action, inter-stimulation, emotional infection and intensification, and other dynamics that always occur when people are in an intimate relation. "Group formation" rather implies a specific group function and relationship in which rules and patterns emerge or are evolved. It implies that each person has a specific functional relation to others or has a specific role to play which results in definite group patterns. This is group fixity and would be unsupportable to patients who need Group Therapy most.

Group formation does appear among people who are in a close relationship for prolonged periods. Wherever there is association, there is also organization. But, this does not apply to therapy groups, a fact that will become clear in Chapters Six and Ten. These groups remain amorphous throughout their existence. The emergence of organization and group control in a therapy group is an indication that at least the majority of the group are ready to participate in regular clubs and should be assigned to such groups which are described as "transitional groups".[8]

To speak of a "group symptom" is equally misleading. Even if it were present in a therapy group, it would be rather difficult to define it. In some one-hundred-and-forty groups, involving some eighteen-hundred children, adolescents and adults, with which this writer was intimately associated, he has seen no evidence of a "group symptom." Symptoms are manifested by individual patients only. Similarly, it is erroneous to talk about "group emotion." The fact that there is emotional infectiousness and intensi-

[8] Slavson, S. R.: Current Practices in Group Therapy, *loc. cit.;* Idem: *An Introduction to Group Therapy,* New York Commonwealth Fund, 1943; cf. Chapter Six, *this volume.*

fication of feelings in a group through mutual suggestion, homo-sexual anxiety, fear of threat and insecurity, does not justify characterizing this as "group emotion." The individuals in each group are still differently affected and respond differently both in quality and degree, even though they may be a part of the total emotional setting. Sometimes one gets a mob reaction; namely, an unreasoned instinctive regressive response of an intense nature, or mobilization of hostility and destructive drives. Perhaps in a mob we come as close to "group emotion" proper as is possible to discern. In a small therapeutic group, however, this does not occur.

By and large, it is an error to speak of "the group" as an entity in therapy. It is always the individual, and not the group as such, that remains the center of the therapist's attention. The group is merely a means for activating individuals and supplying the kind of experience that helps modify feelings and attitudes. This will become clear to the reader later in this volume. To consider the group as a *treatment focus* instead of as a *treatment tool* misleads us as to the aim and means of therapy. In this connection, it may be observed again that there is a large number of patients who should not be placed in groups because of the harm that may result from multiple relationships and tensions.

There has been considerable confusion also in the matter of size and use of the group in psychotherapy. Some practitioners work with large numbers of people, up to five-hundred, to whom they lecture on psychiatry and allied topics, as well as on general cultural subjects. The contents of these lectures and discussions are of great variance. Some therapists use the "inspirational" approach of the revivalist type, while others confine it to well-organized subject matters. Still others limit the groups to small numbers, five to eight, who can, therefore, participate in intensive psychotherapy. An example of these groups will be found in Chapters Seven, Ten and Eleven.

In his study of Group Therapy, Giles Thomas [9] characterizes some of these groups as inspirational and the others as psycho-

[9] Thomas, Giles W.: Group Psychotherapy: Reviews, Abstracts, Notes and Correspondence. *Psychosom. Med.* April, 1943.

analytical, with varying combinations of the two. The future development of Group Therapy as a treatment tool will require considerable clarification on this point. It is felt by those who work in the field of Group Therapy at the present time, that in therapy groups the intimate and person-to-person relations common to a good family should be experienced as far as possible. There is a need for direct interaction among patients, if therapeutic aims are to be achieved. The group, therefore, must be small and the choice of clients and their proper grouping are of utmost importance.

The term "Group Psychotherapy" has been employed also to describe a variety of occupations and activities of mental patients, such as attendance of moving pictures, working in shops, execution of drama in its various forms, spontaneous expression in a group, sociodrama, recreational clubs, music, dance, and numerous other diversions which involve more than one person. It seems to the present writer that this indiscriminate use of the term "Group Psychotherapy" is creating a great deal of confusion in the understanding of Group Therapy, as well as in psychotherapy generally.

That inter-relationships and various occupations can be used as adjuvants in the practice of psychiatry and psychotherapy, is quite obvious and their value as aids in therapy, whether group or individual is unquestionable. Individual psychotherapists in clinics, institutions, and in private practice have employed such occupations as supplementations to treatment, but this does not make them either sole or major therapeutic tools. There is no evidence that group activities in themselves constitute therapy. To achieve intrapsychic changes implied in the term psychotherapy, relationships of the transference nature, emotional freedom and greater intellectual insight are necessary than large-group activities or occupational interests can supply. Group therapists would be on much firmer ground if they reserved the term to specifically planned small groups. To make necessary relationships possible and to gain insight, a therapy group should have no more than seven or eight members, and they should be chosen in accordance with suitability to each other.

The choice of clientele for both activity and interview groups has been discussed somewhat more fully elsewhere by this writer.[10] Here, only a brief statement to this effect can be made.

In activity groups, the aim is to establish *group balance*. By this is meant that patients with varying problems are grouped together so that each may be helped to overcome his specific difficulties; thus, withdrawn and aggressive patients help one another, or the unconflicted member helps one with strong inhibitions to break through his defenses. On the other hand, in interview groups, patients with a common psychological syndrome, who have similar personality problems and are more or less of the same social and intellectual level are most helpful to one another, even though their symptoms may differ.[11] It is particularly essential that contrasts in intellectual capacity should not be too great, otherwise sharing of ideas, mutual stimulation and development of insight would be greatly impeded. In activity groups, on the other hand, difference in intellectual capacity does not affect the therapeutic process.

Thus, it becomes clear that a therapy group must be specially planned. It cannot be a chance conglomerate of persons who happen to have emotional or personality difficulties. Large groups do not meet the conditions required for therapeutic results. One can apply the term "mass therapy" to such large conglomerates of people, but one is hesitant to use the term "therapy" in this connection at all, because it is doubtful whether actual therapy is effected. A large mass of people who live together and share common problems—especially when they live under restricted conditions—accumulate resentment, and grow bewildered and confused. Talking through their problems, thoughts and preoccupations freely is of great value. They are relieved as they gain understanding of the situation in which they live, and participate in planning it. Emotional tensions are diminished as they ventilate their feelings and receive some

[10] Slavson, S. R.: Group Therapy with Children, in *Modern Trends in Child Psychiatry*, Nolan D. C. Lewis and Bernard L. Pacella, Editors, New York, International Universities Press, 1945; *Introduction to Group Therapy*, Chapter IV.

[11] This principle is well illustrated by Mrs. Olive, see *this volume*, Chapter Eleven.

understanding from their superiors, doctors and others in authority. Intellectualization, universalization, dilution of feelings are
great detensors. Such procedures, however, cannot be considered
therapy in the real sense of the word, and the term *group management* can be applied more appropriately here.

Group management is now employed to an increasing extent
in offices, shops and factories. Personnel workers in industry have
found that free expression of resentment and group guidance of
workers increase efficiency and render them more cooperative
and content; but this is a far cry from psychotherapy. Nor do
children and young people who have personality difficulties
receive psychotherapy by virtue of the fact that they are helped
to adjust to a group in a settlement house or camp. Manipulation
of environment and meeting the idiosyncratic needs of the individual do not constitute therapy. At the risk of being redundant,
it may be necessary to state again that psychotherapy involves
at least a minimum degree of more or less permanent modifications within the personality itself that reduce anxiety, hostility
and aggression which originally caused the individual to either
withdraw from or defensively to attack people. Such permanent
modifications cannot be affected by either group discussion or
by manipulating a group setting, even though they help in
satisfying needs and in reducing tensions. One must differentiate
between elimination of acute symptoms and effecting long-range,
permanent changes in the personality.

The subsequent chapters in this book deal with activity and
interview groups with children, adolescents and adults. Activity
groups are used with children and consist of eight boys or girls
selected and grouped together because of the therapeutic effect
they may have upon one another. The first consideration for
grouping is age. Children within an age range of a year and a
half to two years are placed together, except where social, organic
or emotional development indicates the advisability of diverging
from this general rule. Socially over-mature, sophisticated, cor-
pulent or aggressive children may be placed with children older
than themselves, and a younger group may be more suitable for

the weak, withdrawn and frightened child. Extreme problems either of a neurotic nature, of behavior disorder, especially of an aggressive type, psychopathic personalities, and psychotics, are unsuitable for this type of treatment, though experience shows that these non-competitive and non-threatening groups have been very beneficial to children with latent or arrested schizophrenia.[12]

Groups are supplied with simple arts-and-crafts materials and tools to which the members have access and which they can use quite freely. No restrictions of any kind are imposed at the beginning of the treatment. The children also have free access to the total environment and can utilize the furnishings, and other appurtenances in whatever manner they wish. This is a *permissive environment*. Limitations, control, and denial arise naturally as members infringe upon the rights and convenience of others, and, at later stages in treatment, from the therapist as well.

All sessions or meetings end with a repast of simple food, sometimes cooked. Usually it consists of milk, fruit and cake. At table, also, there is complete freedom. Children may eat with the group or take their share and eat by themselves. They may gulp or throw the food around (or at the others) if they so desire. They may grab the victuals, stuff them into their pockets, share with the others, or try to take more than their rightful share. By their own suggestion and choice, the members of the group also arrange trips to museums, parks, zoological gardens, industrial establishments, theaters and opera, and other places that may interest them.

The purpose of these groups is to give substitute satisfactions through the free acting out of impulses, opportunity for sublimative activity, gratifying experiences, group status, recognition of achievement, and unconditional love and acceptance from an adult. Through the activities in the group, children overcome basic character malformations, such as emasculation in boys, confused identifications in girls, feelings of impotence, and

[12] A study of the effect of Activity Group Therapy on a small number of children with latent schizophrenia is now in progress in connection with this writer's work.

fear of expressing aggressive and hostile impulses. In such an environment and relationships, the infantile and overprotected child can become self-reliant and act more mature, the exploited child becomes a more autonomous and self-activating entity, while the rejected child, with the broken-down, weak ego and a low degree of self-esteem, can be built up.[13]

The attitude of the group therapist is permissive. The clients who come to these groups must be convinced that he is a kindly, unpunishing, friendly, yet positive individual. The group therapist is neither domineering nor pampering, nor does he exploit the child for his own emotional needs. Activity group therapists are individuals who have no love cravings or emotional drives toward children that would tie the children down and impede their growth. The children are set free to grow at their own pace through release and the restraint of the others in the group. The result is a new orientation toward environment and people.

The role of the therapist in activity groups is best described as *neutral*. Neutrality should not be confused with passivity. The therapist is not always passive, as will become clear through the description of his work in other chapters of this volume, especially Chapter Six. Though he strives to be as inactive as possible, he succeeds only to the degree to which the children will allow it. The emotional needs of some make them dependent and they come to him for help, consultation, and comfort on the slightest and even on apparently no provocation. Other children withdraw from and do not communicate with the therapist in any way for long periods. He accepts the role each child assigns to him. He is expected to remain outside the emotional flux of the group, so as to allow inter-personal emotional and physical activity on the part of the members themselves.[14] This is necessary, since clients are chosen for group treatment because they need to relate to other children rather than to an adult.

Generally, Activity Group Therapy provides spontaneous dis-

---

[13] This will become quite clear to the reader from the case-material throughout this volume, especially Chapters Six, Ten and Eleven.

[14] See Slavson, S. R.: Some Elements in Activity Group Therapy. *loc. cit.*; also Group Therapy, A Symposium, *Amer. J. Orthopsych.*, October, 1943.

charge of drives, diminution of tension and reduction of anxiety through physical and emotional activity in a group setting that permits unimpeded acting out within the boundaries of personal safety, and through free interaction with fellow-members that lead to a variety of relationships. Inter-personal and social situations constantly arise through which each discharges tensions, expresses emotions, discovers limitations, builds ego strength, finds some satus for himself, develops relationships and a limited degree of derivative insight. The total situation is designed to supply substitute gratifications, give vent to aggression, reinforce the ego, particularly in regard to feelings of failure and inadequacy, counteract deflated self-evaluation, release blockings to expression in some, and build self-restraint in others.

To accomplish all this, the child or adolescent is provided with a tangible social reality with which he deals in accordance with his existing and expanding abilities and powers. Through the experiences in this conditioned environment, modifications occur in his personality through which he acquires strength and facilities for dealing with the outer world and with his own impulses as well.[15]

After some years of practice in this type of Activity Group Therapy, it was discovered that not all children who needed group treatment could be placed in such unrestrained, free-acting-out groups. Some needed groups of lesser aggression density. Younger children, for example, cannot be permitted to act out all their aggressiveness and exuberance, because they first need to establish some degree of self-restraint. What may be described as the *group superego* is as yet unformed. Children with intense neurotic anxieties also cannot endure the display of aggressive hostility without becoming disturbed. Young people in middle and later adolescence do not gain much from arts and crafts in free-activity groups. It is, therefore, evident that no one pattern of Group Therapy can be applied to all types of patients.

With very young children, manual activity may be utilized as a starting point, but the activity itself is not the major treatment

[15] For further description of Activity Groups see Chapters Two and Three. For a detailed description of its practice, Chapter Six.

tool. The child's or the group's behavior is interpreted and insight is given with regard to the motives of his behavior. By these means the young patients are helped to understand their problems. Interpretation and insight come from other members of the group as well as from the therapist. These groups are designated as *activity-interview groups* and *group play therapy* with pre-school children.

One of the types of therapy with which this volume deals is Interview Group Therapy for adolescents and adults. In interview groups, conversations are of the same nature as in individual psychotherapy, but the presence of others with similar problems gives each member support to reveal his feelings and attitudes. The group interviews yield clarification of, and release from, problems, and members develop friendships which they sometimes continue outside of the group. The group therapist helps each member break through anxieties, gain understanding of his difficulties and develop attitudes toward self, parents, siblings, and the world generally. Occasional questioning, direct and indirect discussion and interpretation help each member find release from emotional disturbance, and gain insight into his behavior and reactions.

Because all have common problems and a natural need for one another, group treatment becomes a comparatively easy and natural situation. Adolescents, especially, make ready contact with one another. They are able to share their difficulties with ease and activate one another in expressing feelings and attitudes at a strikingly rapid rate. Once their ego and superego defenses are let down and self-protective reserves removed, they easily reveal their most intimate problems and seem to be almost entirely free of what is commonly referred to as "self-consciousness." They talk in an uninhibited way about prohibited subjects; they expose their hidden feelings about themselves, and repressed hostilities toward parents, siblings, teachers and other persons in their environment, as seen in Chapter Ten.

As shown in Chapter Eleven, adults take a somewhat longer period to overcome their protective mantle of silence, but soon also communicate freely with one another. This is possible for both adolescents and adults because in a group the narcissistic barriers and ego defenses are reduced and they can venture further in the presence of one another than they can in individual treatment. The less conflicted and less frightened group members dissolve fears and defenses—i.e., resistances—in the more neurotic and repressed patients. This is often referred to as the catalytic effect persons have upon one another.

Unlike activity groups, Interview Group Therapy aims at developing in the patient insight into his problems and feelings and at giving him some understanding of the causes of his behavior and attitudes. This is made clear from the case records of group therapy.

As in all other psychotherapy, the dynamics of interview groups consist of (1) transference relationships, (2) catharsis, (3) insight and/or ego strengthening, and (4) reality testing. The transference relationships are vastly modified in their manifestations through the presence of other members in the group —who are in many and essential respects sibling substitutes—as result of which the transference on the therapist is diluted.[16] The patients in the group support each other against the therapist (the father or mother figure) and, therefore, can talk more freely about repressed and guilt-evoking thoughts, impulses, and attitudes. The lessened intensity of the transference on the therapist and the mutual support among the patients reduce the degree of anxiety in each, which in turn facilitates catharsis, and sets in motion the therapeutic process. This is probably the reason for the universally observable acceleration of therapeutic activity in groups. Of no small value is the inter-patient therapy which is fully demonstrated in Chapters Six and Ten. As a matter of fact much more interpretation, including interpretation of dreams, and insight-giving, originates with the patients themselves than

[16] Transference in groups is a complicated phenomenon and studies on the subject are now being carried on by the present writer. It is hoped to make this material available shortly, as well as a more detailed treatise on Interview Group Therapy, generally. See also: Slavson, S. R., Differential Dynamics of Activity and Interview Group Therapy, *Amer. J. Orthopsych.*, April, 1947.

with the therapist. Tentative observations seem to point to the conclusion that the more inter-patient therapy occurs, the better. Patients can accept censure, suggestions, interpretation and guidance from each other with less disturbance and hostility than from the therapist. The latent hostility and aggression that all feel against the parent figure in the group, the therapist, can be easily mobilized and through the processes of induction, infection, and intensification may become difficult to deal with in the group. It has already been indicated that regression to primitive emotions is induced in groups, which constitutes one of the danger points in Group Therapy.

The above should not be taken to mean that hostility and aggression should be prevented or avoided. The very opposite is true. Just as in individual treatment, hostile feelings must be expressed in group treatment, as well, and dealt with therapeutically. But hostility must not become the group climate, though it may be expressed by each of the group members. Only at the point when it becomes infectious and threatens to grow too intense through mutual interstimulation of the members, does it become destructive to therapy. A mob spirit, that results from infectious hostility, is not conducive to insight-giving or any other therapeutic aim one may have.

One of the values of a group, which also serves to prevent hyper-emotivity, is the phenomenon of *target multiplicity*. The target of the patients' hostility is not the therapist alone. Other members (siblings) are also recipients of much of their hatred and anger, which results in dilution of the emotional intensity. Thus it is sufficient to divert aggression from himself for the therapist to become inactive. He can also prevent stimulating negative feelings against himself by remaining passive when he perceives that the group is on the verge of explosive aggression. In practice one finds, however, that as in all cases of sibling rivalry, patients repress much of their hostile feelings against the therapist because they can displace or redirect them to each other. This has minimal therapeutic value and the therapist needs to activate direct expression of hostility toward himself whenever this pattern becomes common or occurs too frequently. One must remember that where there is no discharge of hostility there is no therapy.

One also needs to keep in mind the fact that Interview Group Therapy is in every essential respect similar to individual psychotherapy. The four basic dynamics listed on page 36 are the foundations of all effective psychotherapy, whether individual or group, and it applies to all the types of the latter. It is not possible to further develop this thought in a general work as this, without going too far afield of its central aim.[17]

The reader will observe that no chapter has been included on the treatment of neurotic and psychoneurotic children through activity groups. The present writer had repeatedly urged caution in applying Activity Group Therapy to such patients, since proof of its effectiveness with them was not available. More recent studies prove conclusively that children even with full-blown neuroses improve in these groups provided two conditions are met: one is that the children must be young—below the age of puberty, and the younger the better—and that their neurotic fears do not prevent group association.

Lillian Margolis [18] studied 30 boys who had proved inaccessible to individual psychotherapy and who were placed in activity groups. Of the 30, 14 had successful outcomes and 7 were partially successful. The results that have direct bearing upon our present discussion were those of the 15 boys diagnosed psychoneurotic: 9 recovered, 4 recovered partially and only 2 showed no improvement.

We have instituted another study, as yet not completed, of psychoneurotic children treated in activity groups exclusively, i.e. patients who were placed in groups directly from intake and are still in treatment. Of eighteen such children, all but one showed varying degrees of improvement. In this connection, it

[17] For further material on Interview Group Therapy see Chapters Seven to Eleven.

[18] Margolis, Lillian: Criteria for Selection of Children for Activity Group Therapy, *Smith College Studies in Social Work*, September, 1946, pp. 32-49.

may be recalled that in an unpublished study of a large number of individual cases, Gertrude Goller found that to achieve complete success in Activity Group Therapy "(1) the child must be under thirteen years of age; (2) he must have inadequate social contacts; (3) he must be neurotic or have neurotic traits, and (4) he must be unable to get along with children or have a need to express aggression." [19]

Margolis' table summarizing her findings in terms of clinical categories follows.

Relation of Clinical Diagnosis to Outcome in Group Therapy

Clinical Diagnosis	Success	Partial Success	Failure	Total
Psychoneurosis	9	4	2	15
Primary behavior disorder				
a. With neurotic traits	4	2	.	6
b. Pre-oedipal type	.	.	3	3
Schizoid personality	.	1	1	2
Psychopathic personality	.	.	2	2
Pre-psychotic	.	.	1	1
Character disorder	1	.	.	1
Total	14	7	9	30

This table is of interest also in relation to other chapters in this book.

Primary behavior disorders with neurotic traits which constitute a group of patients for whom activity groups are most suitable (discussed in Chapter Two), improved 100 per cent. The pre-oedipal i.e., children with violent and intense behavior problems, did not improve.[20] Although the number of patients with psychopathic personalities and character disorders are negligible and no valid deductions can be drawn from the statistics alone, the results confirm the deductions made from experience and theoretic formulations. These two types of patients are discussed in Chapters Five and Four, respectively.

[19] Quoted in Slavson, S. R., *Introduction to Group Therapy*, loc. cit., p. 84.
[20] See pp. 44 et seq.

PART II
ACTIVITY GROUP THERAPY

Chapter Two

ACTIVITY GROUP THERAPY WITH PRIMARY BEHAVIOR DISORDERS IN CHILDREN

The clinical category of *primary behavior disorder* connotes conduct difficulties in children "which are primary, and not secondary to disease or defect of the nervous system".[1] Van Ophuijsen speaks of them as the "reactive behavior disorders" because they usually appear in children who react by means of undesirable behavior patterns characterized by hostility and aggression to early emotional deprivation in the family setting.

In such cases we are dealing with children who, in Freudian terminology, have a defective superego formation and whose ego, having been unable to conform to reality during the child's early life, continues to be dominated by the pleasure principle. These children, despite their supposed ego strength as revealed in their aggressiveness and "tough" exterior, were frequently found to have a rather weak ego structure. This could be explained by the restrictive nature of their family background or the fact that their libidinal drives were not brought under control, thus disturbing adjustment to reality.

Primary behavior disorders vary in degree and extent. These variations relate in some measure to the amount of love received in early childhood and to superego formation. We will thus find cases ranging from generally extreme anti-social and egocentric behavior to those where difficulties are present only in limited aspects of the personality. It can be assumed that, aside from

[1] *Outline for Psychiatric Examinations.* Clarence O. Cheney, Editor. New York: State Department of Mental Hygiene, 1940.

43

purely environmental pressures, the individual's constitutional strength also determines the degree to which early deprivations undermine later adjustment.

There are two major groups of primary behavior disorders: (1) the pre-oedipal type and (2) the oedipal type. In contrast to the former which usually stems from experiences before the age of three, the latter originates during the child's oedipal stage of development (age three to six). It includes conduct or habit disorders developing as a result of the child's conflicts in regard to the parents as a couple. Being of more recent origin and presupposing the existence of some satisfying parental relationships prior to the oedipal period, these disturbances are not as intense as those of the pre-oedipal type. Their undesirable manifestations are most frequently focused on the home setting with few problems outside the home. In addition to the behavior disorders, we may also find some neurotic traits in certain of these cases. These are formed in the pre-oedipal period of the child's development and are often caused by inner conflicts in relation to one of the parents (in contrast to the oedipal period).

In general, the treatment efforts with primary behavior disorders are directed toward developing a capacity to establish object relationships in the child, building of a superego and helping him in assuming control over his impulses.[2] As outlined by Van Ophuijsen, individual treatment of these cases involves a re-living by the client of the early disturbing elements in the child-parent relationship and the building up of new, healthy attitudes and behavior patterns. Expecting to be confronted with a punitive adult who would deal with him as the people he had encountered so far, the child instead finds a friendly and warm adult in the person of the therapist. This puts him, in a sense, into a state of imbalance. Lacking justification for a hostile attitude he reverts to a friendly, socially acceptable demeanor. This initial response of the child to the therapist was termed the "surprise reaction;" Slavson refers to the reaction of children to

[2] Van Ophuijsen, John H. W.; Primary Conduct Disturbances: Their Diagnosis and Treatment, in *Modern Trends in Child Psychiatry* ed. by Nolan D. C. Lewis and Bernard L. Pacella, New York, International Universities Press, 1945.

the permissive attitude of the therapist in groups as "a shock." [3]

It does not take more than a few interviews in most instances, however, for the child to reveal his true colors and to behave with the therapist the way he behaves with other adults. He cannot pay heed to the display of warmth by the therapist and he cannot trust him lest he be painfully disappointed again as h had been in his early childhood. Quite on the contrary, the child might attempt repeatedly, through hostile and provocative behavior, to get the therapist to reject him. This is a very important stage in treatment. As the child convinces himself that, while not condoning his "bad" behavior, the therapist is still interested in him as a person, he begins to reach out for a real positive relationship with him.[4] This ever-growing attachment finally comes to a point where the child shows willingness to curb his undesirable behavior patterns to please the therapist who represents the ideal parent figure. Slowly inner controls (superego) are being set up and he is now "willing to give love another chance and to find out that, although there may be hurt, there is also very valuable, desirable gain." [5]

Needless to say, not all cases of primary behavior disorder can be treated successfully by this approach. For a variety of reasons, many children are unable to sustain such treatment relationships given even the most skilled therapist. There are some who are too suspicious of adults and feel too threatened by the very idea of treatment to respond to any personal contact. Others may drop out of treatment later on, particularly at the point when they feel they are asked by the therapist to change their ways. They

[3] See his *Introduction to Group Therapy*, New York, Commonwealth Fund, 1943.

[4] According to Van Ophuijsen, in these cases (unlike in the psychoneuroses) we do not have a genuine transference relationship in treatment, at least not until the very end of treatment. Instead of representing a real person to the child with a primary behavior disorder, the therapist is merely an extension of his narcissism: "a function personified." An object relationship to the therapist is established at the point when the latter has succeeded in making himself truly indispensable to the child.

[5] *Primary Behavior Disorders in Children* (Pamphlet) by Staff Members of the Jewish Board of Guardians, New York, Family Welfare Association of America, 1945, p. 3.

may have been so harshly deprived by their own parents that they cannot bear to take a chance on being disappointed again. The advantage of Activity Group Therapy in such cases stems from the fact that, unlike individual therapy, which uses verbalization as its basic tool, it permits free acting out of impulses.

When entering a therapy group the child becomes emotionally a member of an ideal family unit. According to Freud all groups facilitate regression of its members to an earlier stage of emotional development.[6] This is particularly true in activity therapy groups because of the accepting attitude and neutrality of the therapist which enables the children to express their impulses freely without fear of retaliation. Each member is enabled to regress to the point where he can emotionally re-live the traumatic experiences of his earliest childhood in relation to the group therapist. The therapist assumes the role of the good and ideal (pre-oedipal) parent figure. A similar "transference" occurs in relation to the other group members who become the child's siblings. Invariably, manifestations of jealousy for the therapist's attentions and a desire to be the "only child" will be found in the group. These conflicts are eventually resolved through the mechanism of identification. It is as if the child said: "Since I cannot have father for myself only, I will see to it that no one else has him in his exclusive possession."

It is of interest that numerous children with primary behavior disorders who had been consistently hostile to their individual case workers and unable to relate to them on a positive basis for long periods of time were observed to establish positive relationships in the group with relative ease. We have seen that the relationships among the members in the group dilute the relationship to the therapist and that the members afford each other support and security against the fantasied threatening adult (father). Slowly they become convinced of his real goodness, because he gives them food and materials, helps them with their work, and in other ways displays his interest in and regard for them. Thus an ever-increasing attachment to the therapist is

[6] Freud, Sigmund, *Group Psychology and the Analysis of the Ego*, London, International Psychoanalytical Press, 1922.

established. Nevertheless, as in the case of individual treatment, there will also be periods of negative transference with hostile and provocative behavior aimed against the other group members and occasionally more overtly against the group therapist as well.[7]

As the therapist stands his test and does not fall into the child's trap by reacting to his provocative behavior, the attachment will become even more compelling. At the same time, some of the aggressiveness will be restrained by the other group members. Since he desires the approval and regard of his peers, the child will tend to control his aggressive impulses. The group becomes a satisfying emotional experience in the child's life, and the therapist and the other members assume the roles of objects of identification. With this goes a willingness to curb narcissistic impulses and to modify undesirable behavior in order to gain approval (love) of the therapist (parent figure) and of the other group members (siblings).

The therapist's role in relation to children with primary behavior disorders is fundamentally similar to that of the individual therapist or case worker. At first, this role is supportive and neutral and no direct restraints are imposed upon the children's acting out except those that come from the group itself. After a positive relation has been established, however, and the child feels secure enough with the therapist so as not to interpret any interference as rejection, some limitations are initiated.[8]

It has already been indicated that not all children can be reached through Activity Group Therapy. A desire to be a part of a group, to establish relationships with others, which Slavson has termed "social hunger," is a *sine qua non* for a client to be suitable for group therapy.[9] This excludes the extremely egocentric and impulsive patients who lack the capacity to respond to group influences. Such children, when put into a group, disrupt the therapeutic atmosphere and group balance by their aggressive behavior which can only be checked through authori-

[7] Slavson, S. R.; *An Introduction to Group Therapy*, loc. cit.

[8] *ibid.* p. 164.

[9] *ibid.* p. 15.

tative handling. This would be very undesirable as it would change the children's concept of the group therapist as a warm, accepting and non-punitive person.[10]

Group Therapy is particularly helpful with children who are distrustful of contact with an individual therapist especially when they are referred by authoritative agencies like the Children's Court or by parents who interpreted the agency to the child in a punitive way.

The case of Fred, age thirteen-and-a-half, might be of interest here. He was brought to the agency by his mother who complained of his unmanageability at home, keeping late hours, fighting with a younger sister, truanting from school, and associating with undesirable companions. Fred was born nine months after his parents' marriage, against the wish of his father who did not want any children, but rather desired that his wife continue to work. The home situation had always been a pathological one.

The father was a heavy drinker and a poor provider, who maltreated the children and his wife. He died suddenly, from syphilis, two years prior to Fred's referral for treatment. The mother was an extremely helpless, sick, and quite a dull person. She had no understanding of her own role in her children's difficulties, but blamed her late husband and economic circumstances. She repeatedly threatened Fred with placement in an institution if he did not behave. She told him that he would be getting a "good talking to" at the clinic.

When seen at intake, Fred was so suspicious and fearful that he kept his eyes lowered throughout the whole interview. He would not hear of individual treatment for himself but eagerly accepted the idea of joining one of our "clubs" about which he had learned from a friend. In view of the boy's distrust of adults and of the clinic, it was felt more advisable to place him directly from intake in a therapy group.

When Fred first came he appeared extremely tense and dis-

10 *ibid*. p. 117.

trustful, but soon relaxed markedly and was later able to establish a close relationship with another boy, slightly younger than himself. He has shown some progress in the group, getting a great deal of recognition for his skill and imagination in shopwork. Both the home and the school reported a change for the better in Fred's behavior. At our request he was given special shop classes at school, which enabled him to capitalize on his talents in using tools and materials.

The group therapist reported that occasionally Fred was quiet, tense and morose. The psychiatric diagnosis was primary behavior disorder with neurotic traits and it was, therefore, felt that after a period of Group Therapy, there might be a need for individual treatment when the underlying sexual disturbances which were the probable cause of the anxiety and depression manifested in the group, might be handled.

However, as treatment proceeded, and as a result of a report from the group therapist, this was found unnecessary. Fred had consistently relaxed and became friendly with the children and therapist during the group meetings. The earlier mentioned periods of moodiness had disappeared. This improvement was confirmed in an interview with the mother who reported that Fred was making satisfactory adjustments at home, at school, and in the community. It was therefore not felt necessary to offer the child individual treatment and plans were made to close the case at the end of the group season.

We have seen here a case of primary behavior disorder where the child because of his deep-seated hostility and distrust of adults would not have been able to establish any other treatment contact unless Group Therapy had been offered him. The therapy group offered this child the opportunity of human contacts without the need for entering into deep emotional relationships with either the therapist or the other children before he was ready to do so. As he gained security through the acceptance and warmth of the therapist and the approval of his good craftsmanship by the other children, he was enabled to begin reaching out for object relationships.

The following case is one of a child with rather severe behavior disorder, who received both individual and group treatment.

Joseph was brought to the clinic by his mother when he was nine years old because of disobedience, unruly behavior including temper outbursts, use of vile language, nocturnal enuresis and nailbiting. He was in intense rivalry with an older sister. Joseph associated with a gang of boys who were considered anti-social in the neighborhood. With them, he participated in minor delinquencies. He was inclined to boasting and lying, designed to aggrandize himself. The school complained about his inability to follow classroom routines and about his rebellion against authority. The boy was sloppy and dirty in his personal appearance.

Joseph's mother was an insecure, domineering, and rejecting person, whose handling of the boy was characterized by marked inconsistency. She impressed the case worker as being an essentially cold person, greatly resentful of her role as mother and wife. The father was an immature, passive, and inadequate person who assumed little responsibility in the home. There was marked marital tension, with the father running after adolescent girls in the neighborhood.

The psychiatrist diagnosed Joseph's case as one of primary behavior disorder, with both conduct and habit disturbances.

Joseph had been seen individually by a psychiatric case worker for about a year before he was referred for Activity Group Therapy. While he came for his interviews quite regularly, he seemed to be strongly distrustful and non-communicative. The mother reported a slight diminution in the boy's conduct difficulties at home. When referred for Group Therapy, Joseph was ten years old.

The boy appeared for his first group session well dressed and with his hair nicely combed. He was a well built, dark-haired and dark-complexioned youngster with a pleasant, but rather hard, facial expression. He had a light smile on his lips which seemed designed to cover up his insecurity. He first looked cautiously through the tool cabinet, and then, sitting down at the opposite side of the room with his back to the group therapist, glanced through a picture book. Soon he picked up a racket and started bouncing a ping-pong ball against the wall. The therapist noticed that Joseph occasionally observed him from the corner of his eyes as he did this. While at first reserved in his attitude toward the other boys in the group, Joseph established contact with them during the latter part of the session. He followed some of the other boys in some mild horseplay and engaged in a great deal of childish antics. He had known two of the boys from camp. To the group therapist he talked very little. When he did, it was usually to ask for the same materials another boy had requested previously. During the refreshment period Joseph "kidded around" quite freely with the others. Shortly before the end of the meeting he got into a wrestling match with another boy.

The worker found Joseph to be less well dressed and rather dirty during the next two sessions of the group. He seemed quite restless, running around the room and activating the other boys to clay fights and other aggressive forms of play. He soon became attached to one of the boys, Lev, who had quite a tough exterior. The two boys would spend most of their time together during the meetings, talking, playing games, and participating in various forms of mischief. At the same time Joseph seemed to be in a definite rivalry situation with Lev. He would occasionally ally himself with the latter's opponent when Lev got into fights. Whenever Lev would approach the therapist with the slightest request for help or for materials, Joseph would invariably ask for the same. On one occasion, Lev hurt his finger while using the saw and it was necessary for the therapist to put a band-aid on the wound. Immediately Joseph came over and asked for the same treatment, although the therapist could find nothing wrong with him except an old scar.

During subsequent sessions Joseph revealed a marked interest in food. There would be hardly any session when he would not ask the therapist what the group would have to eat. He seemed pleased when some of the other boys were absent so that he could have a larger share of the food. When some of the boys went out to buy food he would repeatedly leave the meeting room to see whether they had returned. Joseph rarely helped the therapist with the group chores. He was not economical in the use of materials, commencing a number of projects without finishing them. He relied rather heavily on the therapist's help while working.

Joseph's demeanor in the group during his first year of treatment was characterized by a general restlessness and a tendency to constantly move around the meeting room participating in horseplay and inciting the other boys to aggressiveness and destructiveness. Joseph found it difficult to accept new members in the group. He showed his resentment by teasing them and playing tricks on them.

His relationship to the therapist was at first marked by suspiciousness and reserve. He talked in a low voice and hesitatingly, finding it difficult to look straight into the therapist's eyes. Coupled with this was a strong infantile dependency with a tendency to lean on the therapist for help with things he could easily have done himself, and to demand various materials. There was a certain slyness in Joseph's attitude toward the therapist and his occasional smile had a quality of defiance.

By the end of the first year in group therapy Joseph's general restlessness decreased. In his relationship with the therapist some signs of attachment and positive feelings were noted. He showed some change for the better in the care of his person, like washing his hands before eating. Although a good mixer with the boys, Joseph continued to reveal constant and intense feelings of rivalry with them. He showed some interest in playing with fire, he also liked to drill holes in the furniture and made remarks suggesting sexual pre-occupation. He once applied the drill on another boy's buttocks. There was a lessening of his attachment to Lev. Joseph who revealed himself as the more insecure and weaker of the two boys, despite being physically stronger, failed on a number of occasions to draw Lev away from his constructive work with materials. During his first year in the therapy group, Joseph attended twenty-four out of a total of thirty-three meetings.

Joseph continued in individual treatment. There was a short time when he was not seen at all because a transfer to another case worker had become necessary. The boy found it difficult to accept his new case worker, continuing his reserved, non-verbal attitude. He spent most of his time painting the same objects over and over again and playing games during the interviews. He did not talk about himself or his feelings. The case worker felt that the only reason why Joseph came to see her regularly was that he wanted again to be sent to camp which he had enjoyed the previous summer. The mother reported some improvement in Joseph's adjustment at home. Besides being more reasonable in relation to her, he now was wetting his bed only occasionally. However he continued to keep late hours, and developed an attachment to an older man in the neighborhood who owned a garage and seemed to be fond of Joseph. The mother considered this man an undesirable influence upon the boy.

In his second season of Group Therapy Joseph attended twenty-one out of twenty-eight sessions. At the end of this period, the group therapist found him considerably improved. He seemed neater in his appearance and gave the impression of being calmer, friendlier, and more relaxed. He now seemed able to talk freely to the therapist without lowering his eyes. He even gave definite indications of a growing positive attitude coupled with a decrease in his rivalry with the other group members. Joseph occasionally helped the therapist in cleaning up the meeting room and during the refreshment period he no longer grabbed the food as had been his habit in the past. While there was occasional horseplay with the other boys, this did not have the former quality of hostility and provocativeness. At the end of the second year the group therapist reported in part: "During the last three months, Joseph has shown more improvement than during any other period in the group. He seems to have finally been able to accept an adult and other boys, also to give up the need to be hostile and non-cooperative. It is my feeling that Joseph now relates to me well."

A worsening of the marital conflict at home was reported at this time. The mother, who was now being seen regularly by the same case worker as Joseph, seemed bitter and hostile toward the child. Despite the obvious improvement in Joseph's behavior and the cessation of the enuresis, she continued to complain about him, picking on him for slight, inconsequential things. Joseph had not been coming regularly for interviews during this year because there had been again changes in caseworkers. The last caseworker reported evident improvement in the boy's relationship to her which she felt was due to his positive group experience. It was thought that while the same case worker was working with the mother the boy found it difficult to establish a close relationship with her. Therefore, a transfer of the mother to another case worker was recommended to explore her accessibility to individual treatment. So far there had been little change in the mother's attitude and handling of Joseph.

When considering this case from the point of view of the therapeutic process one is impressed above all with the relative speed in which Joseph was enabled to regress to infantile acting out in the group. The so-called "surprise reaction" was of short duration and lasted only for about one session. It is quite possible that Joseph's relatively good behavior during the first session was due to his insecurity in regard to the group setting. His surprise at the unexpectedly favorable attitude of the therapist might have accounted only partially for his behavior. Some of the most important trends revealed in the course of Joseph's treatment in the group seem to relate to an intense sibling rivalry, hostility to the parent figure, and an infantile dependence with marked oral cravings. Most probably these were this child's most significant early frustrations which he was now enabled to relive in the group, but on a different plane, for here he could experience basically warm relationships quite different from those in his own family.

The therapist did not show preference to any of the group members (siblings) and was consistently ready to respond to Joseph's demands for food, for attention, and for love. His aggressive and destructive behavior, his slyness and suspiciousness, became less pronounced as Joseph came to the realization that the therapist was not like his parents: that he need not fear renewed rejection and disappointment. In line with his desire to retain the love and approval of the therapist and the other group members, Joseph began to control his unacceptable behavior in the group; this was carried over, to some extent, to his relationships at home and in the community. The therapist became an object of the child's identification and his superego was strengthened and enriched. The therapist and the others in the group supplied him with substitute gratifications for the deprivations of his early infancy and childhood, and supported his trends toward maturity. A change in the mother's attitude would be of great value, since otherwise the child will be exposed constantly to the same destructive pressures as in the past.

The following case illustrates the problem of a boy with primary behavior disorder of the oedipal type,[11] who was successfully treated through Activity Group Therapy, but where the mother was in need of intensive psychiatric treatment.

Paul was referred at the age of fourteen because of difficulties manifesting themselves particularly in the home. He had severe temper tantrums during which he would attack his parents, and call both of them vile names. There was marked rivalry with twin siblings, four years younger, especially with the girl twin; also, difficulty in getting along with other children. The mother described Paul as dirty and sloppy, nervous, and a nailbiter. He had many food fads of long standing, and slept poorly, frequently grinding his teeth in his sleep. There had been maladjustment at school in the past, although Paul had gotten along well since junior high school. His I. Q. was 121.

The family always had to struggle financially as the father never earned an adequate income. The mother was a tense, anxious, oversolicitous woman, exaggeratedly concerned about food and cleanliness. She herself seemed to feel that she was weak, nervous, and unable to "take things." In attempting to handle the children she would frequently lose her temper, cry and strike them. The father was reported to be more easy-going and passive,

[11] See p. 44 for discussion of oedipal and pre-oedipal types of primary behavior disorders.

an older-looking man who was generally known as "Pop" in the neighborhood.

When Paul was born, Mrs. Kaplan had wanted a girl to name after her mother. The child was not breast-fed, and from the beginning there were many feeding difficulties, including vomiting. Mrs. Kaplan was always very domineering and controlling in relation to Paul, as well as unconsciously somewhat seductive. She was herself an extremely disturbed person, rather preoccupied sexually, and inclined to use the boy emotionally in the place of her husband. It was felt that this mother needed intensive therapy herself and, after a period of treatment, she was referred to a hospital psychiatric clinic. She made some progress there herself and relaxed considerably in her handling of Paul.

Paul was referred directly from intake for exclusive treatment in Group Therapy. He appeared to welcome this eagerly, and made a good adjustment in the group despite his initial anxiety, caution and suspiciousness. After a year of treatment it was felt that the boy had made great strides, within himself as well as in his social relationships. The psychiatrist who reviewed this case stated that the group experience had helped the boy in his drive to become independent of his mother, to master his many anxieties, and to gain a feeling of social potency.

Paul's behavior in the group was described recently as that of a "normal" child. He was secure and cooperative, and had mature relationships with both the children and the therapist, frequently acting as arbiter in arguments without attempting to set himself up as a superior. He was proficient in his use of tools and materials, always planning his work thoroughly and carefully. His attendance was always perfect.

The mother, who was seen recently, impressed the interviewer as being calmer and less harassed. She admitted that Paul no longer presented any difficulties at school or in the neighborhood. The sibling rivalry had become less intense, with Paul spending less time at home, and going out with friends of both sexes. However, the mother continued to complain about Paul's relationship with her and with his father. The interviewer felt that these difficulties were in reality the child's natural reaction to the mother's continued anxiety, over-protectiveness, and inconsistency in handling all her children. She was found to be in need of further psychiatric treatment which would be designed primarily to help her relinquish Paul as a love object. She herself was able to see the need for continuation of her therapeutic interviews.

Paul is a child in whom the preponderance of behavior disorders was a response to faulty identifications in the family setting. Group treatment helped him in building up a stronger ego more capable of dealing with the anxieties stimulated by the mother's expectations of him. Although he now acts very much like a normal boy his age, one can expect some continuation of tensions in the family setting unless the mother can be brought to reorganize her emotional attitude toward her husband and her children.

In conclusion, we may state that primary behavior disorders in children are reactions to early unsatisfactory family relationships, usually involving rejection coupled with emotional and often also with material deprivations. Since there is no internal conflict present, treatment of these conditions primarily involves reliving of the child's early frustrating experiences through a relationship which is basically satisfying and positive. In the course of treatment the child establishes inner controls which aid in curbing instinctual impulses. Interpretation and insight, which are essential in the treatment of neuroses, are of little consequence here.

Activity Group Therapy was found to be effective in the treatment of the less severe primary behavior disorders. The group is conducive to speedy regression and subsequent building up of positive behavior patterns. Strongly deprived children and those with some internalized conflicts may require simultaneous individual and group treatment. Cases of less severe behavior disorders were found to respond favorably to exclusive Group Therapy. At times the parents should be offered individual or Group Therapy, while the child receives group treatment. It is envisaged that Activity Group Therapy will be used for increasing numbers of children with "reactive" behavior disorders.

On pp. 107, 108 the reader will find further description of a number of dynamics through which relationships so essential in the treatment of primary behavior disorders are established in activity therapy groups. There he will find how the patient attaches himself to a series of *supportive egos* who help in his transition from self-indulgent behavior to socialized attitudes and object relationships.

Chapter Three

ACTIVITY GROUP THERAPY WITH EXCEPTIONAL CHILDREN

It is difficult to extract from current literature a uniform definition for the term "exceptional child." Some professional publications insist on a broad interpretation to include all children who are physically handicapped in any way, mentally retarded, or emotionally unstable. In essence, this would characterize any child who deviates from physical, intellectual and emotional norms. Nevertheless, a topical examination of these same publications reveals a preponderance of articles on the handicapped or mentally retarded child only.

The legislature of the State of Texas, in a recent enactment providing for special educational services for exceptional children, defines them as children of "educable mind whose bodily functions or members are so impaired that they cannot be safely or adequately educated in the regular classes of the public schools without the provision of special services."[1]

Many accredited private schools for children use the term in their prospectuses to describe children who require "special handling," while others no longer use the phrase "exceptional child," because they feel that this designation refers to the retarded child specifically.

"Exceptional" is an effective substitute for more stigmatizing expressions such as "slow learner," "handicapped," "problem child," and the like. The original application of the term was probably an outgrowth of honest attempts to spare the feelings of the children and parents concerned, and to reorient the approach to such children in an objective, progressive fashion. The

[1] *Senate Bill*, No. 38, Article 1.

aim of this chapter is not to clarify the meanings of terms, but rather to describe the exceptional child and his suitability for Activity Group Therapy. For present purposes then, the exceptional child is considered to be one who stands apart from others because of specific physical and intellectual limitations. Invariably, such children are forced to bear the burden of social stigma as well.

At an early age the exceptional child is made sensitive to the stigma that sets him apart in varying degrees from other children. Upon entering school, he is further sensitized. The schools contribute in large measure to the process of accentuating the limitations of these children. Almost universally, the prevailing administrative practice is to segregate these children from the "normal" ones. The child who is physically handicapped finds himself with other similarly afflicted pupils in a special room. The dull child also becomes part of a "special class" with a different teaching program. This approach, aiming to meet the peculiar needs of exceptional children, actually widens the gulf between them and others of more normal constitution. What should be a significant socializing experience becomes a restrictive, stigmatizing one.

The difference between the dull child and others is generally less marked when removed from the classroom. What may be described as "social intelligence" tends to place children of different intellectual capacities on a common plane in other than scholastic areas. In play or conflict, the retarded child may use aggressive, colloquial forms of expression with facility. This tends to camouflage his shortcomings and to reduce the elements of difference between himself and the others. Some children find a measure of relief in this way, but many find that segregation in school is reflected in more extensive social rejection. Most children accept established patterns, even those of the school, and unwittingly exclude many exceptional children from participation in recreational activities after school. The dull child often becomes "labelled" with the various astringent titles that unfeeling children invent in prolific fashion. The physically handicapped child finds few opportunities to express himself even in a limited way in games. This complete or partial ostracism by other children is among the most disturbing experiences for them. Isolation is followed by frustration and a sense of defeat.

In the home, the exceptional child may, and often does, suffer rejection. Parents unconsciously project their own weaknesses on the very children who need encouragement and acceptance. Unconscious guilt feelings become translated into unsympathetic and critical treatment. Parents of these children cannot accept them, because they are a source of guilt and are a threat to the parents' own security and social status. The situation in the home is often even more aggravated by the presence of more normal or even superior siblings who emphasize the deviations of the less fortunate child. Many dull children are faced with the unhappy experience of being constantly compared to their more favored siblings.

Reactive behavior patterns must inevitably develop as defensive measures to protect the child's ego against the rejections and frustrations of school, playmates, parents, and siblings. The distorted personality traits that result are determined largely by the quality and intensity of irritating environmental factors, and the constitutional strengths or weaknesses of the child himself. He may withdraw from social contact or become provocative, aggressive, and hostile. Occasionally the dull child may receive some status in the group by extreme behavior. He may capitalize on his dullness and accept the jibes and "kidding" of his comrades in exchange for a negative degree of security. To maintain the position of the group buffoon, he must always be on tap for some queer or distorted infantile performance to satisfy the sadistic leanings of other children, while the physically handicapped child may attempt to conceal his impediment by theatrical, extravagant acts. The resultant pattern, be it histrionic excess, passive withdrawal, or aggression, merely accentuates the personal liabilities of such children and emphasizes the need for treatment.

Children with extreme mental retardation or incapacitating physical disabilities are not acceptable for treatment in the ordinary activity therapy group, but the presence of one exceptional child or even several in the same therapy group with other children of normal or superior intellectual and physical capacities does not impede the progress of the group as a whole. No special treatment method is used that would serve to accentuate the limitations of the exceptional child. The organization of each therapy group is carefully planned so as to place each child in the group that will best meet his needs. Particular caution is exercised before placing the exceptional child.

The basic principles upon which Activity Group Therapy is based meet the needs of most maladjusted children, exceptional or otherwise. We have seen that the permissive atmosphere of the therapy group enables children to express themselves freely. Behavior, devious as it may be at times, is accepted without comment or criticism by the therapist and, because of this, also by the other children.

This is made possible by the fact that the therapist is a source of praise, ego support, and love (acceptance). His personality and attitude are such as to convey to each child a feeling of complete acceptance and unconditional love.[2] The disturbed child gains little from verbal assurances alone. The trite expression: "Actions speak louder than words," is particularly meaningful to the anxious child. The therapist must be sensitive to the needs of the children, gentle in approach, equable in temperament and primarily a person honestly fond of children. This attitude is gradually adopted by the group members toward each other. His tolerant manner slowly causes a diminution of anxiety in the children and greater tolerance toward each other.

Although at first a child may be distrustful of the new unfamiliar freedom and it may stimulate anxiety for awhile, the therapist's attitude and later that of the other children reassure him.

The "inferior" child sometimes tries to possess the therapist, and to monopolize his attention. This is an outgrowth not only of his need for the exclusive attention (love) of the therapist, but also a real need for help because of personal limitations. The demands for the attention of the therapist are often excessive and

[2] Slavson, S. R., *Introduction to Group Therapy*, New York, The Commonwealth Fund, 1943, pp. 6, 140.

may bring the child into conflict with others in the group. The therapist must contrive wherever possible to satisfy these demands without making the other children unduly aware of it. He remains throughout psychologically neutral, consistently kind, helpful, and tolerant with all.

Emotional imbalance is often accompanied by feelings of inadequacy and incompetence. The ego structure of the disturbed child, attacked from within by unresolved elemental impulses, is further threatened from without by enforced isolation imposed by his playmates. Whether he withdraws or attacks, he usually retains his social hunger.[3]

Thus, Activity Group Therapy has as one of its primary goals the development of a feeling of self-esteem and ego strength. The immediate satisfaction that the child experiences in the therapy group stems from the realization that he "belongs to a club." Although others in the group may express resentment and challenge him, he still has a measure of security in his primary feeling of membership, supported by the therapist. He has been invited by an adult, written to by the office, welcomed by the therapist! The therapist oftens hears such a child exclaim in the heat of argument: "Yeah? Well, I belonged before you did!" This in itself is a source of only temporary security. It is the ultimate acceptance by the group that is fundamentally effective in strengthening his ego. The therapist must subtly support the weak child until he can achieve status in the group.

Feelings of self-esteem are further stimulated by careful praise from the therapist and later from others in the group. The crafts materials are graded in difficulty so that each child, the exceptional included, can achieve some measure of success through work with them. A child will often spontaneously volunteer such information as: "Gee, I never knew I could do this;" or, "My mother asked me to make it for the house." The latter remark was made by a boy whose mother had rejected him in preference

[3] Slavson, S. R.: *loc. cit.*, p. 15. This is best described as an impelling need to be accepted by his peers, to do as they do, dress as they dress, and to maintain status in the group. Without this need the child would not respond to treatment in a group.

for a younger sibling. The exceptional child seems more overtly gratified by recognition in the group than do the others. Perhaps more than others are such children aware of their own peculiarities and therefore have a sense of isolation.

Trips to places of interest are particularly valuable in promoting feelings of achievement and strength. The children usually pick their own destinations or activities: a theatre, museum, zoo, rowing, ferry ride, and the like. Children feel especially confident after traveling with a group. They become better acquainted with the far-flung resources of a large city and derive much satisfaction from traveling by subway or elevated trains. After several such trips, one child told the therapist that he now knew how to get home. This was quite an achievement for this particular boy.

The child with feelings of inadequacy is particularly in need of some form of creative expression, and the arts and crafts materials in the groups are carefully selected to meet his needs. Clay, leather, paints (finger, tempera, enamel), plastic materials, colored paper, linoleum, embossing paper molds, weaving supplies, copper, lumber and other materials are at his disposal and he can use them as he will. Games such as checkers, tenpins, badminton and pingpong are also available. Many of the children display latent talents and creative abilities of high order. Standards for accomplishment are set by each child for himself. He works at his own pace and frequently discovers that he possesses a higher level of skill than he first believed.

What is perhaps of even greater value is that the child establishes contact with others as he works.

The child takes home the things he makes and very frequently he gains new status at home because of it. Father may appreciate an ash tray; mother may use a small change purse, and both may as a result give him more recognition. Many of these children present objects they made as gifts to case workers, teachers and friends. As donors of their own creations they feel important. Thus the creative output of exceptional children is often of particular value for gaining acceptance from parents and friends. All too often the abilities of dull and handicapped children are minimized because they had never been given access to the proper creative outlets.

Many of the members of the group recognize that the "club" is a special one, insofar as it is composed of children who have "had some trouble," as one child ingenuously expressed it. There follows from this mutual identification, which in a sense furthers the child's feeling of "belonging," and thus, in turn, the exceptional child in the therapy group is often spared the embarrassment to which his limitations ordinarily subject him elsewhere. This, in particular, is a significant experience for him, for it is in sharp contrast to the segregating practice of the school.

Handicapped children require more help than others in relating to the group and this imposes a greater burden on the therapist. He must exercise extreme caution not to stimulate jealousy and rivalry. His natural tendency to protect the weak child must be curbed, for by doing so he would give the child in question only a temporary respite from group hostility. This would also threaten the therapist's position in the group.

The following three histories summarize cases of exceptional children who were treated in activity therapy groups. One was mentally retarded, the second had a neurological defect and physical handicap, and the third was physically grotesque.

Robert was referred for treatment by the Bureau of Children with Retarded Mental Development. His I. Q. on the Stanford-Binet and the Kuhlman-Anderson tests respectively was 77 and 78. He was in a special ungraded class for children with retarded mental development. His teachers reported him as inattentive, listless, and quarrelsome. The psychiatrist felt that the boy had an "incipient schizoid personality."

Robert was twelve and one-half years of age at referral. He was taller than average, frail and anemic looking. His face was drawn and pinched. He held himself upright with seeming effort. His personal habits were far from acceptable. His clothing, of poor quality, hung loosely, accentuating an otherwise unprepossessing appearance.

Robert was the third of four children. An older brother and sister, both of high intelligence, attended college. A younger brother, a bright, normal child, was the parents' favorite. Robert's mother, an extremely dominating person, set very high standards for him. The father was less rejecting, but markedly impatient with the boy and often drew comparisons between him and the other siblings. Robert presented the picture of a mentally retarded boy with marked feelings of inadequacy and insecurity. He was withdrawn and anxious and could not relate to children of his own age.

Treatment was first instituted on an individual basis, but the interviews were on a superficial level. Largely because of the boy's intellectual limitations, supplementary treatment in Activity Group Therapy was found necessary.

Robert attended therapy groups for three and one-half years and his attendance was excellent. The group, where the children were his own age, interested him from the start. At first he sought to establish himself in the group through ingratiation, but instead he activated the hostility of the others. His intellectual and manual inferiority at first heightened his feelings of inadequacy, but he seemed fortified by his relationship with the therapist, as a result of which he became more secure and able to resist the onslaught of the other boys.

Within the year after treatment began there were evident signs of improvement. Because of his assertiveness, he became more a part of the group. He engaged in games with the boys and made steady progress in the handicrafts. It was obvious that he was developing increasing confidence in himself.

Concomitant improvement was observed outside of the group as well. Whereas formerly his acquaintances in the neighborhood were children several years younger than he, he now played with boys of his own age. He learned to ride a bicycle in the therapy group, an activity that formerly had been extremely frightening to him. Robert told the case worker that membership in the "club" was one of the most important things that had ever happened to him, and recognized that he had improved a great deal in his relationships with the boys in the club and with other people.

The case worker, who continued seeing the boy on a supportive basis, described Robert's progress as "startling," and the boy was transferred soon after to Activity Group Therapy for exclusive treatment.

In spite of Robert's limitations the therapy group had enabled him to become less fearful, more confident of his abilities, and more secure in his relationships with people.

Martin was referred for treatment by the educational clinic of a local college. He had been under treatment at the guidance bureau of the city schools for several years. Psychometric findings over a period of years revealed unusual variability in mental functioning. He obtained an I.Q. of 75 on the Wechsler-Bellevue Intelligence Scale. On the Stanford-Binet test his I.Q. ranged from 75 to 103. Additional tests revealed an achievement level equal to that of the fifth grade, two years below his grade placement. Martin was fourteen-and-a-half years old when referred by the educational clinic. He was a tall, fairly attractive boy with no unusual physical defects. He wore glasses to correct a serious visual deficiency of one eye. His clothing, of average quality, was usually in fair condition. Martin was injured at birth. Neurological examination indicated "encephalopathy, perhaps congenital or associated with birth trauma." An electroencephalogram pointed to the possibility of a static lesion of the brain. The discrepancy in ratings on the various psychometric tests also pointed to a traumatic brain injury.

The referral statement indicated that Martin was in difficulty both in school and at home. Current symptoms included temper tantrums, infrequent soiling, and crying. His problems in school began the very first day he attended with his running away. The difficulties recurred each term as he moved to a new class. The school complained of inattention and lack of cooperation in routines.

Martin's mother described him as an aggressive, hostile child. She herself obviously had little affection for her son or his younger brother, age three. Martin clashed frequently with his father who openly preferred the other sibling. Many infantile patterns characterized Martin's behavior at home. During his temper outbursts he yelled at and cursed his mother. His eating habits were infantile and he had many food fads. He wanted his mother to feed him. Martin had no friends or social outlets. Most of his spare time was occupied with playing by himself or with listening to the radio for hours on end.

The problem, in brief, was that of an intellectually limited adolescent boy with a deeply rooted, infantile character structure, complicated by overt parental rejection and intense sibling jealousy. Because of his limited capacities, it was deemed inadvisable to attempt direct therapy with him. Recommendation was made for placement in Activity Group Therapy.

Martin attended the therapy group for about one-and-a-half years. He was accompanied by his mother to the first session. After that he came alone, although he expressed fear of traveling, particularly when it was dark. Martin was at first extremely dependent upon the therapist. His manner was ingratiating and some of the boys resented this. He was also limited manually and in working with the simplest craft materials constantly solicited help from the therapist. He was jealous when the therapist helped other members of the group. To one boy he became particularly hostile. This rivalry situation seemed a direct reliving of the home situation.

Martin sought to monopolize the therapist, and the other boys reacted to this by telling him bluntly to "try doing your own work once in a while," and referred to him as the "pest." The group pressure gradually took effect, and Martin made fewer demands. Because of this, the other boys accepted him more and became more tolerant of some of his infantile actions. Now that he no longer monopolized the therapist, he turned more and more toward the other boys. He often badgered them in a whining, plaintive manner. He would request tools from the boys, and refused to relinquish them even though he had no use for them.

As Martin became more secure in his relationships with the therapist and more confident of his status in the group, a more direct approach was utilized by the therapist. Martin was subtly and indirectly thrown back on his own resources. The therapist sometimes pretended not to hear a request for help or merely pointed in the general direction of the supply cabinet when Martin asked for tools and materials.

Martin now joined freely in discussions with the boys and traveled home with some of them. His fears of traveling in the dark diminished. His eating habits were now normal and he no longer soiled his clothes.

Treatment in the therapy group was terminated after a year-and-a-half. Because of the boy's basic infantile character, the strong possibility of organic brain injury and eye defect, it was thought that he had gained as much from treatment as was possible. Evaluation of treatment progress indicated improvement in several important areas. Motivated by a desire to emulate others in the group, his appearance and personal habits improved. He developed facility in traveling alone about the city. His fears had disappeared. The acceptance he found in the therapy group strengthened him to a point where he was able to build up a better concept of himself, and his relationships with other people improved. Through a secure relationship with the therapist, he was enabled to relinquish some of his infantile patterns.

Jack was nearly twelve when referred for treatment. His adjustment in school was poor both in achievement and social relationship. Although his I.Q. was 100, he was retarded several grades and had difficulty with subject matter even at the lower grade level. He had no friends, in school or out.

Jack was an only child. His mother, a serious cardiac, was also neurotic. She was infantile and dependent and treated her son like a grown young man. After the death of her husband, when Jack was eight years old, she imposed upon Jack a masculine role he could not fulfill. Their relationship was mutually dependent and on an infantile level.

Physically the boy presented a brutish, animal-like appearance. His body was peculiarly disproportionate. His torso was 'ong and almost rectangular. His arms and legs were short and stubby and seemed to have been added as an afterthought. A large, misshapen head rested squarely on his shoulders with little semblance of a neck. Jack could be described as an "exceptional child" by virtue of his appearance alone.

Treatment was instituted on both casework and Group Therapy basis. Jack immediately established a close, dependent relationship with the group therapist. This characterized his relationships with all adults—mother, case worker, group therapist and others. He constantly sought the therapist's attention and aid. He was indecisive about the most trivial things and tried to get reassurance from the therapist and the other boys. His inability to coordinate muscularly resulted in sloppy, disorganized work with the crafts materials. When he used paints, as he did almost exclusively in the beginning, they were inevitably brushed on everything near him, including his clothing.

The boys, for the most part, seemed to recognize Jack's limitations and accepted him. Occasionally he was teased or attacked by another boy and he relied to some extent upon another more aggressive boy in the group for protection. He often remained close to the therapist to ward off an anticipated attack.

His dependence upon the therapist persisted for many months. He remained unskilled and unimaginative with respect to the materials but almost imperceptibly began to expand his interests to include woodwork, clay and leather. In spite of the crudity of the objects he made, he always expressed satisfaction with them and received praise from the therapist. He also began to defend himself in more positive fashion when attacked, and the boys who had teased him before developed respect for him. Jack was very enthusiastic about the "club," and gradually, as his confidence grew, he became less dependent on the therapist and more outgoing with the children.

After a year-and-a-half of treatment, Jack developed enough security and strength to accept membership in a local community center. He spent some time after school earning money by running errands for neighborhood storekeepers.

The therapy group environment is of low social pressure, with

no emphasis on intellectual achievement or manual dexterity. The complete absence of any formalized educational procedures removes anxiety on this score. The fact that the therapist makes no distinction in his relationships with the children emboldens the exceptional child who thus feels more closely identified with the others in the group. When freed from the restrictions and pressures of every day life, the retarded child relaxes emotionally and responds almost eagerly to the tolerant, permissive atmosphere of the therapy group.

It is sometimes advisable to place the exceptional child in a therapy group with children younger than himself. The age difference helps him in making social adaptations. As he grows better equipped to handle himself, he is transferred to a group his own age. This graded social reality provides experiences commensurate to the child's strength.

Chapter Four

ACTIVITY GROUP THERAPY WITH CHARACTER DEVIATIONS IN CHILDREN

"Character" is one of the controversial concepts in psychology. There is a considerable diversity of definitions of the term. Some use it as a specific construct, others interchangeably with personality. This is largely due to the fact that character has both sociological and psychodynamic connotations, for in everyday language character means strength, power, capacity, morality. When one is said to have character, the implication is that he is strong or honest, or both.

However, personality and character do not seem to be the same. "Personality, as we understand it, is a positive concept, while character is relative. It implies social judgment and is externally conditioned. Personality is permanent and inimitable in its very nature, for it is made up of all the latent and the observable physical and mental dispositions and capacities. Character, on the other hand, results from development and modifications of these in accordance with accepted social principles and morals. . . . Character . . . has to do with controlled functioning according to a series of principles." [1] Cyril Burt defines character as: "the sum total of those personal qualities of mind which do not constitute, or are not pervaded by intelligence. They are marked by feeling rather than skill." A. A. Roback conceives character as "an enduring psychological disposition to inhibit instinctive impulses in accordance with a regulative principle." Thus, we see that

[1] Slavson, S. R., *Character Education in a Democracy*, New York, Association Press, 1939, pp. 150-151. Character is discussed in this volume as control, as adjustment, as disposition, and as discipline.

psychodynamically, character is that part of one's personality with which one deals with inner and outer reality. Freud suggests that character is the balance between the instinctual drives and the controls of the ego. Reich sees character as the total mechanisms in an individual for "avoiding unpleasure, . . . establishing and maintaining a physical equilibrium . . . and . . . absorbing repressed energies." Kardiner suggests "basic character" as an outcome of adaptations to a cultural pattern and social demands in which the individual lives. Fromm speaks of "character structure" in terms of a product of the social milieu. Fenichel considers character as "nearly identical" with ego. While each of these and other writers emphasize some specific aspect, it would seem that character is a result of constitutional predispositions and the many and varied dynamic forces within the personality in its interaction with the outer world.

Reich's concept of character comes closest to our own, and conforms most with observation of the growth and development in children. Character can be defined as the totality of the adaptive mechanisms with which the individual deals with his instincts, drives, anxieties, and the demands of the outer world. It is, according to Reich, "a specific way of being of an individual, an expression of his total past." There is little doubt that apart from the constitutional qualities and predispositions, character is acquired through the struggle of outer and inner necessities of living in dynamic interaction during the growing stages of the individual. By this we mean that given, let us say, a dominating and restricting parent, the child can grow up into a person who is suggestive, pliable and has little autonomy; or he can grow rebellious, stubborn, independent and overly self-reliant. The choice an individual makes in developing these two contrasting patterns is determined either by additional environmental factors—supportive relations, or the lack of them—or by constitutional predispositions, or both. One can respond either by submissiveness—by giving up part of his ego—or he can insist on autonomy and self-determination. The final result is a pattern or mechanism specific to the individual for dealing with psychic forces within, and the demands and pressures without. Character, according to Fenichel, is "the habitual form of a given reaction, its relative constancy." [2] Thus, we hear of characters that are compulsive, neurotic, submissive, passive-feminine, hysteric, narcissistic, and of numerous others.

Elsewhere[3] we have described a character pattern determined by the fact that when, for specific reasons, a boy in a family continues to strive to replace his father in the affections of his mother, his character becomes "over-mature". He behaves like an adult, is intolerant of childish acts, dominates children, insists on proprieties and on socially acceptable behavior. Contrariwise, a girl who seeks to replace her mother in her father's affections becomes flirtatious, over-conscious of her appearance, exacting in her dress and emotionally shallow. Similarly, in accordance with pressures and experiences, one's character can become inhibited, restricted or constricted,[4] or in Fenichel's words: "Any offensive instinctual impulse, nearing realization, may provide a spiteful reaction in some persons, passive compliance in others, truculence in others, and so on." [5]

Character, then, can be conceived as being the equilibrium between the ego and the libidinal strivings, the sublimating and repressive systems within the psyche, primary strivings and their gratifications, repressions and reaction formations, and the numerous psychodynamic and psychosocial forces operating in the life of the individual. It is the manner in which one resolves his oedipal conflict, establishes identifications, develops mechanisms of avoidance and aggression, the role he is forced to assume in relation to siblings, parents, and other persons of significance in his life. However, the most distinctive feature of character is the *quality* of the behavior characteristic of any one individual that distinguishes him from others. It is for this reason that the identity between character and ego would be difficult to establish. The

[2] Fenichel, Otto, *The Psychoanalytic Theory of Neurosis*, New York, W. W. Norton, 1946, p. 467.

[3] Slavson, S. R., The Treatment of Aggression through Group Therapy, *Am. J. Orthopsych.* July, 1943.

[4] *Idem*, The Treatment of Withdrawal through Group Therapy, *Am. J. Orthopsych.* October, 1945.

[5] Fenichel, *loc. cit.* p. 467.

ego is a *dynamic* system within the psyche, while character is the summation of many factors, static and dynamic, which results in a specific way of dealing with life.

For the present purpose we shall accept this as our foundational concept of character. A wholesome character is one in which the individual deals with situations in life and with his own impulses efficiently. This means that adequate energy is available; that it is neither excessive nor insufficient to meet the demands. of a situation, and that the manner in which the energy is used produces the least displeasure to all involved. A weak or restricted character is one that cannot mobilize sufficient energy to deal with situations to the best advantage. This may be due to actual organic deficiency, fear of aggression, or to withdrawal. On the other hand, some persons discharge more energy than a situation requires. This is the quantitative aspect of character. There is also a qualitative side, however. The difference in quality colors one's character, such as hostility, affability, poise, excitability, compliance, or indirection.

If we conceive character as the resultant of two sets of forces— the external demands and inner pressures—we must accept the fact that it is shaped by experience. If this is the case, we can safely assume that since character is determined by experience with reality, it can be set aright through series of corrective experiences. This is especially true of children. The character of a child is still in the process of formation, his identifications are not fixed, and being psychologically labile, experiences are absorbed and tend to modify the total personality. Children's responses and their mechanisms for dealing with instincts and anxieties, are changed by conditions much more easily than those of adults.[6]

Observation of a rather large number of young children indicates that character changes can be effected comparatively easily in children by favorable relationships and experiences. Even neurotic character traits and anxieties are sloughed off, as the young child's ego is strengthened, and he grows more capable of dealing with his instinctual drives. Unless the child has been

[6] See also Chapter One, pp. 19-20.

seriously damaged, he naturally develops associations outside of the home and to an increasing degree becomes a part of the larger world. It is at this stage that experience, which has such a telling effect upon his character formation, is also effective in correcting it. However, one cannot be as optimistic about adult patients whose neurotic distortions are severe and where a full blown neurosis exists. They require a type of individual therapy that involves transference and insight.

We have already indicated that Group Therapy is an experience in autonomous living and a special type of association. The patient can behave in accordance with the state of his development. He can discharge his drives, impulses and hostilities. As in all other types of sound psychotherapy, regressive behavior is not only permitted but encouraged. Infantile fixations can be acted out and realistic reactions to it are supplied by the other members of the group. The child has numerous opportunities to change his negative perceptions of himself and to discover his strengths. It is for these and other reasons that Activity, Play, and Activity-Interview Group Therapy are particularly valuable in correcting undesirable character traits and other psychologic malformations in young children.

As an illustration of some of the theoretic concepts suggested here, several cases will be summarized. The first case history is that of a passive-feminine boy treated through Activity Group Therapy.

Herman, twelve years old, the youngest of four children, the three others being girls—aged twenty-two, twenty and sixteen—was accepted for exclusive group treatment. His youngest sister, a very disturbed girl of sixteen, was a patient of ours under individual treatment for an obsessional neurosis. The mother, a person of limited intelligence, was openly hostile to the sick daughter, and probably rejected all the other children. She was described as very disturbed, withdrawn and lethargic, frequently unable to follow the trend of a conversation as though she forgot in the middle of a sentence what she was saying. The father, eight years older than his wife, came to this country at a mature age and apparently made a poor adjustment to his new environment. His earnings were low and the family depended for financial support on the older daughters. Very little more was known of the father, except that he seemed to be a mild person who represented the symbol of a good parent to both our patients. There was a history of considerable quarreling and conflict in the home, largely instigated by the sixteen-year-old girl who was under treatment. It seemed that Herman was repeatedly involved in these squabbles and participated actively in them.

Herman, being the only boy in the family, was the favorite child and was markedly over-protected by the mother, but he seemed to have a closer relation with the father. The mother was overtly infantilizing and limiting Herman's activities, and even at the age of fourteen and fifteen, when he was able to develop interests, she circumscribed his activities because of her fear that he might be injured. She would not permit him to go skating or bicycle riding and hampered him in his efforts to participate in other occupations normal to a boy of his age.

He spent a summer in camp before joining the therapy group where he was found to be passive, compliant, considerate of others, and submissive to everyone. He was described by two independent observers as being effeminate. The family described Herman as lackadaisical, dreamy and in a state of lassitude. At about the time Herman was referred for treatment the father died, which upset the boy greatly. Several months elapsed after his father's death before he joined the group.

At first, his attendance in the group was guarded. He did not respond to the invitation to the first session. After attending twice, Herman absented himself at alternate sessions for a few months. Then he came to three successive sessions, and thereafter absented himself again. He repeated this pattern until the end of the group season. He seemed to be afraid of his own voice, spoke only in a whisper, and seemed frightened when the therapist spoke to him in ordinary conversational tones. Therefore the therapist spoke to Herman particularly caressingly and quietly. Toward the end of the season, in the early summer, Herman came to five consecutive sessions. In the Fall when the group reconvened, he again displayed fear of the group, but once he began to come he attended twenty-five sessions without one absence.

At the very first session Herman attended, the therapist found him standing in the middle of the room, hat in hand, looking visibly frightened, with his face distorted as in pain. Though the therapist's friendly and encouraging attitude reassured the boy somewhat, he did not remove his coat and continued to hold his hat in his hand. He took a position in front of the closet in which materials are stored, thus turning his back on the group. As the therapist or a boy came to the closet for tools or materials, he would sheepishly step aside. Throughout the subsequent sessions that he attended, Herman continued to look very anxious, "screwing up his face almost in a knot," appearing frightened and very worried.

It was characteristic of his compliance that, when at one of the early sessions Sam, another boy in the group, grabbed Herman's ankle and waltzed him around the room, Herman followed his aggressor around like an automaton, hopping on one foot, with a half-hearted attempt at a smile. It appeared as though he waited until Sam would tire of his game. His attempts to work with materials later on were half-hearted and usually his projects remained unfinished. Herman was particularly disturbed by the hyperactivity of the other boys, and when they were fighting or rough-housing, appeared to be frightened, clenched and unclenched his hands and cracked his fingers.

For a number of sessions, the boy did not stay for the refreshments, that is to say he usually remained from forty-five minutes to an hour instead of the customary two hours. It seemed that the direct proximity and the communal relation during refreshments were too threatening to him. However, four months after he joined the group, he overstayed the usual time by half an hour.

Another illustration of his fear and compliance was evidenced by his behavior when he did begin to participate in the refreshments with the other boys: he would not reach for anything on the table or ask for food. He just sat quietly until someone would think of passing the food to him. When any of the boys wanted something that Herman happened to possess, he readily gave it up. He once had two binder posts, for example, which he needed for his own job. When another boy needed one he gave it to him, thus making it impossible for himself to finish his own project. On occasions when the therapist offered to purchase materials that Herman needed, the boy would be embarrassed, saying that he would buy them himself. He had little contact with any of the other children, keeping strictly to himself.

The "progress report" four months after the boy had begun attending the group, stated: "At the last meetings, Herman's reticence greatly decreased. He engaged in a prolonged and serious conversation with Sam (the boy who made him waltz around earlier in the year) about school and teachers. On another occasion, he and Sam were wrestling and Herman's face expressed definite and unmistakable rage. This was the first time the boy showed any feelings. At another time, when Sam tapped Herman lightly on the shoulder, the latter ran after him to return the tap. The contrast to the frightened, withdrawn boy of early meetings is a definite sign of improvement." Herman's face was now relaxed, he smiled occasionally when the therapist or other boys talked to him. He asked for assistance when he needed it from the therapist, and occasionally spoke with some of the other boys.

After thirty meetings, the therapist described Herman as straightforward. His general demeanor had improved greatly; he now carried himself erect, and moved around the room freely. He engaged in discussions with the other boys and offered his views unhesitatingly. It was upon his insistence that the group went for its first bicycle ride. He was very proud of learning to ride a bicycle, and took particular pleasure in similar trips later on. Four or five bicycle trips were held that winter. After one of these trips Herman came upon a group of three acquaintances with whom he walked home. On another trip he let a boy from his neighborhood ride his bicycle. On two occasions, Herman asked permission to ride the bicycle in his own vicinity, where he could be seen by his neighbors.[7]

That summer, the camp report again described Herman as a quiet boy presenting no problems, except that he day-dreamed very frequently. The counselor commented that Herman displayed a desire to have friends, but did not know how to approach boys. Herman did not smile, seldom talked and shied away from groups. It seemed that a new group reactivated his shyness and though he regressed, he did so to a considerably lesser degree than the previous summer.

At the end of his second year in the group, the therapist reported that Herman had made approximately thirty ration book holders, five or six small coin purses, eight or ten different kinds of key cases. He was quite animated when he worked. Particularly was he activated when the meeting was coming to a close and he was working on four different items at the same time. He rushed about to finish them all before closing time. On one occasion he took a definite stand against the group on the matter of a trip, insisting on his point. He was as yet too weak to compromise. This was a great improvement for a boy who only a year and a half before was so frightened of group situations that he readily gave in and complied.

At about this time, Herman acquired a friend, a boy slightly smaller than himself, but tougher, who according to Herman's own statement, handled the "fighting needs" of the relationship. The therapist also noted that there had been considerable improvement in the boy's relationship with the other members of the group and with himself. Herman now smiled broadly and talked cheerfully and freely. He beamed with delight when the therapist called the attention of the other members to one of Herman's handiworks that was especially attractive. Herman now demanded that the therapist spend all the money that the office allots to the group.

At approximately this period Herman graduated from junior high school creditably, and went on to high school. He found the

[7] The same desire for testing himself against his environment and "show off" was displayed by Murray. See Chapter Six.

adjustment in the new school somewhat difficult, particularly did he find algebra troublesome. He had expressed an ambition to get into one of the city colleges. The mother reported that he liked the "club" very much and got particular satisfaction out of being able to make things with his hands. He was fifteen years and two months old at the time of this report.

In an individual "follow up" interview with the boy at this time, he was found chafing under his mother's overprotection. He had to sneak out for bicycle rides and rowing, and spoke of his friend whom he described as a rough boy. Herman expressed his intention to go to work during the summer, as well as after school hours. He did not wish to go to camp because he thought that the boys there would be too young for him. A few months later when interviewed again in relation to camp, he expressed delight that he was now able to "convince" his mother that she did not have to worry about him when he went bicycle riding and rowing in the park. He had made a bag and leather set in the group for his favorite sister.

When, during the summer, he found himself staying in bed as late as twelve o'clock, he decided on his own to get a job, despite his mother's discouragement. He secured a position with a manufacturer, whom he knew from the neighborhood, who paid him eighteen dollars a week. At first, he said, the work was easy but after a while the women workers asked him to carry heavy bundles and he felt that they were taking advantage of him because he was the only male there; but he "stuck it out" through the summer. When the question of algebra was again taken up and a suggestion was made that he get a tutor, he said he would prefer to do the work without help. Herman was also planning to work after school hours despite his mother's objections. He was pleased with the fact that he was able to get his mother "bit by bit" to stop babying him and to allow him to go to places and do the things that he wished. He still had to get her to allow him to buy his own clothes. Last time, when he went to buy a cap his mother insisted that he buy one that he "despised." He argued with her until she let him buy the cap he liked.

A Rorschach administered when the boy was fifteen years and

eight months old, indicated that his personality had a schizoid quality and that "in spite of his helpless exterior the test shows more negativism than his behavior suggests. His slow reaction time seemed due to an attempt on his part to prolong his negativism. Actually, he seems to be very much in control of the situation and usually puts up a good job of fooling people."

The psychiatrist who was consulted also had felt that there was a possibility of a schizoid personality here, but that group treatment had been of great help in tying up the boy with reality and had probably prevented progressive development of the schizoid trend. Herman attended seventy sessions out of a possible eighty-three, most of the absences having occurred at the beginning of treatment.

The case worker who had seen the boy to follow through on his adjustment, had been the caseworker in camp two summers before. He reported that, compared with the boy's earlier appearance and behavior, Herman seemed greatly improved. He now was robust, much healthier looking, friendly, and related easily in the interview. When seen again seven months later, the boy reported that he had found a job for himself as a bus boy in a restaurant in another borough of the city about forty-five minutes travel from his home. To do this, it was necessary for him to tell his mother that he went to the movies. He had, however, confided to his twenty-three year old sister, who was his favorite.

Herman's character when he came to us had been shaped by (1) faulty identifications, (2) the manner in which he had resolved his oedipal conflict, (3) avoidance mechanisms he had adopted, and (4) the feminine role he was forced to play in the family situation. These factors were superimposed upon a basically schizoid personality.

Herman was the only boy in a family of three girls, a domineering mother and a weak father. He was, in addition, the youngest in the family. Thus, his primary identifications had been established with non-masculine models. It was therefore natural that he should adopt passive traits, and probably develop fantasies about phallic women. This had caused a withdrawal of his psychic energies and a development of avoidance mechanisms. Through the latter, he prevented evoking aggression against himself, which he perceived as dangerous to his security.

Because of the family situation, he had related closely to his father, a weak person, who was also under the domination of the women in the family. Here, too, he identified with a passive-feminine character. Thus, Herman's early life was devoid of the aggressiveness associated with masculinity in our culture. The role he was forced to play was, to a great extent, that of a girl.

In addition, Herman had to build up defenses against the pressures in his home. These defenses took the form of a self-protective withdrawal.[8] He perceived his environment as threatening, and in order to prevent attack, he assumed a manner of non-provocation. To act out or to express his emotions meant to activate counter-aggression against himself, which he wished to prevent. The therapist had recognized strongly repressed hostility in Herman. We reported the incident of Herman's playful wrestling with Sam, when his face expressed intense rage. The Rorschach test revealed this as well. Herman's quiet exterior, according to the Rorschach, was disguised negativism. We may call it a retaliatory hostile mechanism. The adaptive patterns by which the boy dealt with his inner drives and external pressures, were resolved and corrected through the group experience.

Character can be conceived as a form of limitation, namely, it is a definite and permanent way of behaving, specific to the individual. In young children, it can be changed more or less easily because of the child's flexibility and capacity to readapt himself. The group had helped Herman overcome his character limitations by (1) permitting him to bring forward his hostile aggressiveness without fear of retaliation; (2) supplying new models for identification in the persons of the other boys in the group and of the therapist; (3) helping him overcome his fears to break through his emotional and psychological incapsulation, and (4) encouraging him to play out the masculine role which he had had no opportunity to do before.

[8] See Slavson, S. R., Treatment of Withdrawal through Group Therapy, *loc. cit.*

It must be noted that treatment in this case was not directed toward resolving any neurotic elements that may have been present. Although Herman did not display specific symptomatology, and although we did not become aware of an unusual degree of anxiety, apart from his worried facial expression observed early in treatment, it is conceivable that the boy may have been subject to some such anxiety. Certainly, the history of this boy would warrant such an assumption. It was felt, however, that the boy's adjustment difficulties were resolved without dealing directly with whatever neurotic elements were present. He was strengthened to a degree that enabled him to deal with his life and his environment.

Schizoid personality may be a result of constitutional factors, and psychotherapy in such cases can affect the superimposed difficulties due to environmental pressures, but not the constitutional deviations. The fact that a child seems different from other children since birth tends to further emphasize the difficulties.[9] Withdrawal as a reactive pattern can be corrected by Group Therapy. It has been our experience with many withdrawn children, whether constitutional or reactive, that the superimposed state can be removed through treatment and a change in character achieved.

Herman, for instance, has reached out for relationships in and outside of the group and has shown improvement in other areas. We need not fear, therefore, any deterioration, or further withdrawal, at this point. The fact that he passed through puberty without a reactivation of his difficulties is also a favorable sign. We believe that in such cases, Group Therapy is indicated, because of the stimulation of the sense of reality and of the object relationships the group supplies.

Because of the limitations of space, only the high-lights of the following cases will be given.

Arnold, an only child with superior mechanical abilities, was referred to Activity Group Therapy at the age of thirteen, as a seclusive child who had no friends. He did not play with children

[9] See Chapter Three.

and spent most of his free time at home, tinkering with mechanical objects. He was very defiant, aggressive and rebellious against his mother, but had a fairly good relation with his father. A partial albino, he wore glasses, had poor eyesight and attended a sight conservation class in school where he was doing acceptably well. In the neighborhood and at school, children called him names and occasionally attacked him. He was not able to defend himself, but instead ran home, crying bitterly.

He attended fifty-four out of a possible sixty-one sessions. At first, he followed the pattern of behavior gleaned from his history, namely, he made easy contact with the group therapist, but was evasive with and distrustful of the boys. He secluded himself from the group by working with arts and crafts, at which he was adept. After a brief period, Arnold became more outgoing and provocative, but readily submitted when other boys retaliated.

In a follow-up study, a year after Arnold had joined a therapy group, the mother felt that some of his difficulties of which she had complained, had disappeared. He was now able to fight his own battles and did not come home crying, asking her to defend him. When the boys called him names, he fought them. He had also learned to travel long distances by himself. Despite the fact that two years before, he had been very unhappy in camp, he was very enthusiastic about the "club." Arnold expressed particular enthusiasm for the group's activities. He had acquired an electric jig-saw at home, like the one the group used. He had friends in the neighborhood but they were, as he said, "fair weather friends." They played with him only when he was around but did not call for him. In school, he had much better friends. (This, too, was a new development.) In fact, when he was ill with pneumonia, some of these friends came to visit him, which pleased him greatly. One of these friends is now going to high school with him.

In his second year in the group, Arnold seemed considerably more relaxed, but now tended to act out the other extreme. He annoyed and molested the boys, though in a playful manner, and used force to get the things he wanted. When he became too hilarious, he was restrained by the therapist.

At a subsequent "follow-up" interview, the mother reported that Arnold retained the progress he had made. He was successful in school, having passed all subjects. He was then in the second term of high school, but still in a sight conservation class. The children in the neighborhood were now afraid to attack him or say a "bad word" since he was now "quite able to defend his rights." The mother reiterated Arnold's enthusiasm for the therapy group.

In the last interview with the mother and the boy, which was held two years after he had joined the group, the boy was described as generally friendly and relaxed. He said he now had "plenty of friends" of whom at least six were very close, and he was able to travel to various places in the city alone. He had worked part time in a bicycle shop, but was now in business for himself. He bought old bicycles, remodelled them, and earned at least five dollars on a deal. People in the neighborhood seemed to seek him out when they had bicycles to sell or wanted them fixed.

Toward the end of the interview, Arnold himself summarized his original difficulties. His problem had been that he had had no friends and had felt very unhappy about having to spend his time in the house playing by himself. Now that he had friends he was quite content and did not feel any further need for help.

We shall have to forego, at this point, the interpretation of this case, except to indicate that we were dealing here not only with the beginnings of a constricted character, but also with a defective personality caused by an organic inferiority. Being stigmatized and "different," the boy developed fears of normal associations. He was not withdrawn, but rather isolated. Through the status he gained in the permissive social atmosphere in the group, and through his manual skills, his disposition toward isolation was corrected and a change in his characteristic behavior effected. Note should also be taken of the understanding he gained of his problem, and the change in him. This is designated as *derivative insight*.

The case of Pearl is in some respects similar to that of Herman, and the following is a very brief summary of a three-years' treatment in an activity group, in which basic character changes occurred in this girl:

Pearl, a dull-normal girl, was referred for psychotherapy at the age of thirteen by a hospital physician who had been treating her for headaches, dizziness and loss of weight. Physical findings proved negative. The girl also complained of toothaches and stomach-aches.

Pearl was the third of five children, ranging in ages from eleven to twenty-three years. The father, a habitual drunkard, was out of the home serving a jail sentence for attempted rape of Pearl. The mother was a good-natured, healthy, easy-going person of dull mentality. She was fond of the children and had a wholesome, free flowing and affectionate relationship with them.

Individual casework treatment revealed that Pearl was strongly identified with her mother and protective of the younger sister, to whom she actually harbored a good deal of repressed hostility. She was fearful of the day her father would be released from jail when she would have to face him. School was a problem because the mother, to whom she clung for protection against the father, refused to take cognizance of the child's intellectual limitations as against her manual dexterity. She was forced into an academic program above her intellectual capacity.

The somatic complaints disappeared under individual treatment. She was referred for Group Therapy early in contact, because she presented a withdrawn, shy and demure character. Activation by a group was considered essential. In addition, the caseworker found that, because of this girl's intellectual limitations, no insight could be given her.

When the father returned home, Pearl found that she could deal with the situation. She wished to withdraw from individual treatment, but expressed a desire to continue with the therapy group.

Pearl's behavior when she began to attend the therapy group was that of a shy, timid, submissive, frightened girl. She came to the first session accompanied by her older sister. During the first year, she remained unaggressive, always waiting to be asked to come along, never taking the initiative. She rarely spoke except when addressed and kept herself occupied with crafts materials with which she was exceptionally adept. She came to every session, and it was observed that she gradually became more relaxed. Although she still was a follower, she was beginning to take a somewhat more active role in the group, and as the girls became aware of Pearl's manual ability, she became more and more in demand for help with their work. Pearl gave assistance very freely and willingly. She soon participated in group chores and took the initiative in telling two girls that they ought not to fight during meetings. She began to verbalize more, told of her fighting with her younger sister and even conspired with the group therapist to keep the latter from joining the group. Toward the close of the year, Pearl defended herself when one of the girls began fighting with her. On this occasion, she held off the girl, saying: "So you are going to fight with me, are you?" and succeeded in warding her off.

She was still considered too withdrawn, shy, and easily influenced and managed by others. She continued to ask the therapist for permission to take home her finished products, saying that she knew she could take the things home, but she liked to ask permission. She was warm and friendly when she said good-bye to the therapist at the last session of the year. Pearl said that she was glad she had met her; that she hoped the therapist would have a pleasant summer, and that she would see her again in the fall.

In the fall, the girls continued calling upon Pearl for help with their work. Shy and timid as she was at first, this recognition of her ability seemed to convince her of status and acceptance. She would then assert her superiority by saying: "Now, you know how to do that. I'm not going to help you anymore", or "I'll help you some other time." However, she did help them.

On one occasion, one of the girls opposed Pearl's pouring milk for the group. Pearl grabbed the bottle, refused to give it up and won her point. The group therapist also noted that she had acted with greater confidence and spoke more freely. She spoke of boys and expressed an interest in dancing. With a girl-friend, she attended a dance at the settlement house where the therapy group held its sessions. She said she enjoyed these dances.

Although she always was clean-looking and neatly dressed, she now began wearing brighter dresses, ribbon bows in her hair, and on one occasion, she had bells on her shoes. At the close of the second year, the therapist described Pearl as having become quite mature, able to make decisions, and to give constructive criticism to others; she had become one of the central persons in the group, with definite leadership qualities.

When the group convened again in the following year, Pearl adjusted easily to the new group therapist and some of the new members. Now in her third year of treatment in the therapy group, and past fifteen years of age, she made an "excellent adjustment" and the new therapist noted that Pearl was "very pleasing, self-confident, friendly and at ease in the group with all the girls and with the therapist, and that she sometimes even dominated the group." She took the initiative in group activities and discussions, expressed opinions and preferences and participated in group decisions. She volunteered to go on errands for the group, inviting other girls to join her. On occasion, she would censure girls for behavior that she did not feel acceptable, such as flirting with boys or calling them from the window of the meeting room. Pearl initiated group games as well as some playful rough-housing. When she won all the nuts in a game she initiated, Pearl divided her winnings amongst the girls. She now frequently sang and laughed and reacted to situations in a completely natural manner.

She grew socially sophisticated, smoked, spoke of boy-friends and talked about her social activities. In a "follow-up interview" with the mother, it was found that, except for her difficulties with the academic subjects in school, there were no criticisms of the girl. The mother talked in glowing terms of Pearl. She was pleased that Pearl was quite mature now, popular with young people, and had perfectly satisfactory social outlets, giving no trouble or concern to the family. Pearl brought home her boy-friends, and had them call for her when they took her out.

Furthermore, Pearl and her older brother, who were always fond of each other, very frequently went out as a foursome. Whereas in the past Pearl tended to be a drudge, she now had become too absorbed in social activities and not quite as helpful with home responsibilities. Nevertheless, she still frequently helped her mother. The conflict between Pearl and the younger sister had diminished. The younger girl also had found friends of her own.

In analyzing Pearl's problem we found that although she suffered from conversion symptoms, these were not of a truly psychoneurotic nature. They were rather reactions to her fear of her father's sexual advances and probably also to pregnancy fantasies. They were essentially activated by a realistic situation and her disturbance was justified, rather than of an imaginary or neurotic nature. What concerned us most, however, was her general maladjustment to her environment, social inaptitude, compliance and dependence upon her mother, all of these being in her case a part of her character. The mother was a kindly, infantile, easy-going, though very dull person, who gave her children much security, but at the same time tended to tie them to herself. Pearl's image of herself was one of inadequacy and to some extent, also of helplessness. Her compliance constituted a real risk, especially in the neighborhood where she lived, which was one of the major delinquency areas in the city. It was, therefore, necessary to counter-act the restrictive and impotenizing influences in the home, which Pearl had now incorporated into her character. We had to find some means of activating the natural flow of her energies, help her perceive herself as capable and strong, and overcome the fears of her aggressions that were kept in abeyance by her mother's attitudes.

The group helped Pearl find herself, as it were. Her timidity was eliminated through the support of the therapist, through identification with the more outgoing girls and, especially, by the fact that she was the most skillful craftsman in the group, making others dependent on her. All this strengthened her enough to assert herself, resist pressures from the outside and grow generally more balanced. Her self-reliance was well manifested when she later stubbornly persisted in her refusal to go to school, where she failed because of her limited intellect, and when she insisted on going to work and supporting herself. In a follow-up study several years after termination of treatment, it was found that Pearl had been self-supporting, that she was now married and was making a good adjustment.

We shall now present a case under treatment in *Interview Group Therapy* [10] as a further illustration:

Rhea was referred for treatment at the age of fifteen because she was withdrawn, felt inferior and inadequate, had no friends and frequently stayed away from school. One of the most disturbing problems with this girl was that she was late for all her appointments, as well as for school. Rhea explained her absences from school as caused by her fear of going into the classroom late; therefore she preferred to stay away entirely. The chief problem that the mother recognized was that Rhea was "too quiet;" she had no other difficulty with her. Under treatment, a number of other rather serious personality problems of a neurotic nature came to the surface.

The group met once a week and the sessions usually lasted one-and-a-half hours, frequently extending beyond this set time. During treatment, the girl revealed that she felt inadequate, inferior and unattractive, though actually she was rather pretty. Feeling as she did, she neglected her personal appearance, and was sloppy. This had improved as a result of group treatment. Rhea's I.Q. was 83, and a Rorschach examination given about a year after treatment had begun, revealed that she was "emotionally immature, childishly naive, resisted growing up and assuming responsibilities. She enjoyed the protection afforded to a little girl, although the prospect of maturing seemed not altogether unpleasant to her. In the test, she compared herself to a caterpillar blossoming out into a beautiful butterfly. She had some Cinderella-fantasies."

[10] See Chapter Seven and Chapter Ten for discussion of Interview Group Therapy.

Although we were aware of deep-rooted oedipal involvements, strong hostility to the mother and a desire to displace her, we devoted ourselves at the beginning to helping the girl mature. In the group, Rhea consistently came late and the girls, with whom she later developed a very good relationship, chided her and demanded that she come on time. Rhea was characteristically quiet and was once described as a "yes girl" by the others. As the discussions proceeded, however, she was able to express her views and after six or seven months, became a participating member of the group.

During an "inventory discussion" at which each of the girls talked about herself, Rhea said that she did not "act right" and explained that she did not have enough "self-confidence." She now recognized the fact that she felt secure in being a little child and therefore refused to grow up. Both her attendance and her direct verbal expression revealed the fact that she had a strong desire to be with the girls and seemed to prefer those girls of the group who had problems of family adjustment similar to her own. However, they were much more mature and these identifications and her desire to emulate these girls helped her to adopt more mature means of dealing with situations.

She later complained that she was being treated "like a small child" at home; that her father did not permit her to remain unguarded in the house, and added: "This makes me feel funny." Rhea became more aware of her personal appearance, dressed more appropriately and neatly, and began to apply rouge and lipstick.

This growth, however, created a conflict in her and she expressed it in the following way: "Should I disappoint my parents, who seem to find it hard to see me grow up, or should I stay a baby and please them?" This was clarified to her in discussions with the other girls. Some time later, Rhea expressed her pleasure in the fact that it was the "group that helped me act and feel more like my own age".

During many discussions the girls in the group helped her realize that she was undecided as to whether she wanted to continue acting like a little girl or grow up into maturity. One of the examples they used was her coming late, her irresponsibility and her impulsiveness in relation to boys, whom she now began to seek out. During one such discussion Rhea admitted that she would like to be "half and half" (half child, half mature). At about this period, she related a dream which revealed that whenever she got into difficulty, she again became a tiny baby, thus definitely revealing her tendencies to regression.

At seventeen, about two years after treatment had been initiated, Rhea presented a considerably more mature picture in every respect. She took complete responsibility for the home during her mother's frequent and prolonged absences in hospitals; she came on time to the group and now saw her past as living in "suspended animation" in relation to time. She now had become thoroughly and fully aware of time and the need for punctuality. She no longer stayed away from school, but came to classes promptly and was now in her graduation class in high school. This raises the question whether the result of the intelligence test was not too low, because of her general immaturity.

Since a number of the girls in the group were under individual treatment by the same therapist, a discussion was held as to the relative value of the two types of treatment. Rhea was quite positive in expressing herself in favor of group treatment because, she said, "the group helped me to understand myself better." Although some deep-rooted and underlying problems in this girl were not resolved, her characteristic manner of escaping into infantile behavior and fantasy were corrected.

It became evident that Rhea was ready to take her next step in treatment, namely, to tackle her relation to her parents, especially to her father. In fact, at one of the latest sessions, she questioned why she was more responsible for the management of the home when her mother was in the hospital, thus indicating that she was becoming aware of her rivalry with her mother. Having overcome her infantile attitudes and feelings of unworthiness, she also brought out some of her feelings about her father.

At a Rorschach administered two years after the first one, we found that the girl was "more responsive, freer, able to express herself easily, and her feelings of inferiority as well as her self-consciousness were greatly reduced. She responded more maturely. While she still had oral sadistic fantasies they were not as infantile as they had been before." The two Rorschach tests were administered by two different psychologists and confirmed the impression one received from the girl's general adaptations.

Chapter Five

CONTRA-INDICATIONS OF GROUP THERAPY FOR PATIENTS WITH PSYCHOPATHIC. PERSONALITIES

The material in this chapter is not intended as a contribution to the controversy on the nature and dynamics of "the psychopathic personality." This clinical category is still in the process of being defined, and will probably not be fully clarified before considerable psychosomatic studies will have been made in relation to organic inferiorities as they affect social adjustment, and before more tangible understanding of the term "constitutional factors" will have been evolved. We can recognize the psychopathic personality, however, by characteristic social adaptations and by the manner in which the individual deals with situations in his life. In fact, so characteristic is this social adaptation, especially characterized by irresponsibility, that the term "sociopathic" as the more correct designation has been frequently suggested. Different writers have variously described the type of personality now designated as "psychopathic" by various terms such as moral imbecility, social insanity, psychopathic states, constitutional psychopathic inferiority and other designations of a similar nature. Despite this variety in nomenclature, all agree that such individuals are impulsive, narcissistic, unreliable, irresponsible, emotionally labile, quixotic, limited in affect, superficial, and free of visible anxiety or guilt.

Though much still remains to be done to arrive at an understanding of it, considerable work on the nature of this character structure and its causes has already been done. It is now possible to identify some of the mechanisms in the "psychopath." Being unable to meet the pressures of life and the demands made upon him, he finds compromise, as everyone else does, in the executive areas of his personality. The fact that these techniques deviate from the normal, remains unknown to the psychopath himself. He seems to lack the faculty for moral judgment. Thus, his life is characterized by "lawlessness, disregard of social mores, rules and regulations." Lacking the capacity for relationships, the psychopath remains narcissistic and selfish with little or no consideration for others. The predominant drives in his life are self-preservative. He has little or no regard for the group's welfare and can deal with social demands only within the narrow limits of his capacities.

Such persons, following the biologic drive for survival, adopt mechanisms for dealing with people and reality on a narcissistic level. They are self-centered, with little or no regard for persons or groups. If conditions require it, they adopt indirection, dishonesty, cleverness and other similar escape techniques. The difficulty in dealing with such persons is that their facade is always pleasant. Being emotionally shallow, they are usually friendly, are good mixers, adaptable, and make pleasant company—all on a superficial level. Persons with whom they come in contact have no way of discovering the personality lacks that lead to this pleasant facade. It is only upon close association that one finds them to be irresponsible, unreliable, exploitive, inconsiderate. It takes considerable time before one recognizes these qualities under the exterior of charm and *savoir faire*, and unfortunately, one does so only too late.

Some hold that psychopathy is a result of definite constitutional defects that make "normal", or socially adequate, adaptations impossible. These writers insist on including in this classification only persons with such defects. Common sense leads one to the conclusion that an individual, constitutionally and organically inadequate to bear up under the stress and strain of everyday living, would develop the kind of adaptive patterns and attitudes with which he can deal with life in his own peculiar way. Since he is limited or conditioned by his constitutional reserves, the psychopath would of necessity evolve adaptive methods within his range or quality.

More recent understanding of the psychopathic personality and its structure, however, points to defective early relationships as a possible cause of psychopathy as well. In her investigation of a small group of private patients diagnosed as psychopathic personalities, Phyllis Greenacre [1] found that early relationships seem to be the cause for this type of character development and the resulting behavior. One of her striking findings is that the fathers or the grandfathers of these patients had been prominent and respected persons in the community. They were emotionally distant from the patients and, therefore, their value as sources of superego development was low. Among the parents and grandparents were persons in public trust and in authority: clergymen, judges, heads of schools, civic leaders; and in humbler walks of life: policemen, detectives, truant officers. The mothers of the patients were over-indulgent; they had a narcissistic attachment to the patients and the separation of the child and the mother had not been accomplished. Greenacre also indicates that the exhibitionistic components of the child's narcissism had been greatly exaggerated in the family, largely by the mothers.

For the purpose of our present discussion, it will not be necessary to deal with the further implications of these relationships and the dynamics that may operate in the development of the psychopathic personality; nor is it necessary for us to settle the problem as to whether the psychopathic personality is constitutionally determined or environmentally conditioned. It is commonly accepted, for example, that homosexuality is a psychopathic state of constitutional origin, though there is room for disagreement here as well, since homosexuality may be a neurotic manifestation resulting from early identifications and an inverted oedipal conflict.

What is important for our present purpose is to explore whether or not persons with this type of character development can be reached by a group, especially by activity groups. We know that Group Therapy is effective only with individuals who have a need to be accepted, to belong with other people, who place a premium upon the recognition and relationships they can develop

[1] "Conscience in the Psychopath," *Am. J. Orthopsych.*, July, 1945.

in group settings. They have a need for others, which we have described as "social hunger." [2]

Obviously, this craving for relationships is only an extension of the earlier relationships in childhood. We have seen that unless there is such a homonomic foundation present, groups, as therapy, are counter-indicated. Without this foundation, the patient simply continues to act out his narcissistic patterns and does not modify his feelings or capacities for relationships. We are unable to postulate on the basis of our observation that the psychopath has no social hunger. In fact, we found that psychopathic patients attend group sessions very regularly and that their rate of attendance is high. They seem to enjoy themselves hugely and appear to gain a great deal of pleasure from the experience. If we were to consider satisfaction and attendance as criteria for therapy, we could easily be misled as to the value of groups to such patients. The enjoyment of the group by these patients is derived not from the pleasure of improvement, or better adaptations with other persons, nor from the acceptance by the group and the therapist. The pleasure seems to arise rather from the narcissistic, self-indulgent use they make of the group, usually through provocative acts. They are disorderly, break rules, irritate and provoke fellow members and challenge the adult in a veiled fashion. This focuses attention upon them. The behavior of some of the boys in this category is overtly aggressive and disturbing; others may be destructive by less obvious means, such as breaking of furniture during the absence of others in the room, and stealing. It is not altogether true that psychopaths are devoid of anxiety. They can be made anxious, but this anxiety is not derived from the conflict with the superego. In the absence of an adequately developed conscience, this conflict is at a minimum. The psychopath becomes anxious, however, when he is directly threatened as to his status or security. Bernard, who will be described presently, was most concerned with the fact that his parents would discover his failure in the group and beat him. He begged the group therapist not to reveal his dismissal to

[2] Slavson, S. R.: *Introduction to Group Therapy*, New York, Commonwealth Fund, 1943, p. 15.

his mother and father, and when finally discharged, he used various means to cover up the fact. His anxiety did not stem from guilt or conflict; it was rather the fear of his father's punishment.

But the fact that he was so disturbed created doubt in our mind as to our course of action and we consulted the referring case worker, who informed us again that Bernard was diagnosed as "very neurotic" and that a Rorschach given him revealed a deeply repressed anxiety. The discovery of deeply repressed anxiety in Bernard made us only more cautious. Because anxiety is associated with neurotics, one must go to all lengths not to intensify it in activity groups. In interview groups, anxiety states can be used in the therapeutic grist. The patient can talk about it. The conversation with and the attitudes of the therapist and the other members serve to allay it, but in activity groups the patient cannot get such relief or acquire direct insight.[3] It is therefore essential that the therapist should not appear as a punitive agent.

One, therefore, wonders whether the current assumption that the psychopath is free of latent or repressed anxiety is justified in fact. Unless one accepts the claim that psychopathy is entirely a result of constitutional factors, one has to recognize the fact that the psychopath, because of relationships in his home, rejected in early infancy the authority of the adults, refused to internalize their code, and repressed the concomitant anxiety. This would explain the psychopath's defective superego formation and emotional shallowness. It is therefore understandable why a Rorschach test may detect repressed anxiety.

As a result of our experience with a number of psychopathic boys, we do not accept for treatment children and adolescents who have psychopathic personalities. Experience has indicated that they are not accessible to this type of treatment. However, despite careful screening such clients occasionally do escape detection, largely because of the inadequate history available or an error in diagnosis.

As an illustration of the inaccessibility of the psychopath to

[3] Slavson S. R.: Differential Dynamics of Activity and Interview Group Therapy, *Am. J. Orthopsych.*, **April, 1947.**

group treatment two cases will be summarized: one, in which the narcissistic and disturbing behavior was overtly expressed, the other, where aggression and destruction were less manifest.

Bernard, diagnosed as a psychoneurotic, was referred to us at nine years of age, after a period of individual therapy in which no progress was made. He was described as imaginative, restless, aggressive but not hostile, and unable to conform to routines. He was particularly disturbing in school and in other groups to which he belonged where he was making a very poor adjustment. He was said to be "not exactly malicious," but rather to "act as he pleased" and much of his behavior could be interpreted as "attention getting." He had a characteristically winning manner, and was sturdy, wiry and extremely good looking; the youngest of four boys in the family, the others being eleven, fourteen and nineteen years old. The mother was an infantile person, inconsistent in the handling of Bernard although she seemed to have "considerable warm feelings toward him." The father was irascible, an economic failure: having been an actor at one time, he had finally wound up as a factory worker. He had had a number of "nervous breakdowns" with depressions, but refused psychiatric help. He was more rigid and strict with Bernard than with any of his other children, and beat him a great deal.

After the very first session of the group in which he acted in a very narcissistic manner, disturbing the group considerably, and provoking the therapist, it was our feeling that the diagnosis of Bernard might be psychopathic personality, rather than psychoneurosis. We observed him for two more sessions and acting on our hunch decided to restrain his behavior, which we would not do with a neurotic patient. When he proceeded setting fires, messing up the room needlessly, and indulging in similar behavior, he was told to stop. Bernard did not respond to mild restraint, however; direct prohibition was necessary. At this, Bernard seemed quite upset and burst into tears.

Surprisingly enough, Bernard's behavior greatly improved as a result of the pressure by the therapist. After six or seven sessions, however, he resumed his old pattern. His behavior again became increasingly more difficult, to a degree that it threatened the existence of the group. The last of the seventeen sessions, from none of which he was absent, was characteristic. Bernard walked around the room aimlessly, looking for a few minutes into all the closets. Then he walked over to Robert, another member of the group, and grabbed a board on which Robert was working. After a tussle, Robert recovered his board and Bernard continued walking around aimlessly and yelling: "Order in the court!" Later, he took out cleansing fluid from the closet and turned on the electric stove attempting to set the fluid on fire. When the therapist removed the fluid from his hands, Bernard did not resist and began running around the room in circles. He then ran up impulsively and cut across all the material for cork mats, rendering them useless. He continued walking aimlessly, stopping at each one of the boys to see what he was doing. After this, he ran over to the therapist's raincoat which was hanging on a clothes tree, and attempted to punch holes in it with a paper punch. The therapist took the punch from Bernard, who said with feigned politeness: "Excuse me." He then walked over to the materials closets again.

Later, during the refreshment period, Bernard piled up all the crackers before himself, leaving none for the others. This gave rise to a general tussle at the table. Before leaving he packed in a box the food that was left over, saying to the therapist: "Let me take the cheese home. I will give it to my pet mouse."

Bernard had not developed any relationships with any of the children in the group, in spite of his faithful attendance. He never helped with the chores nor cooperated in any way, but was rather a threat to the other members in the group. He developed no positive feelings for the therapist; instead, he was provoking and often contemptuous of him. When informed by his case worker that he could not continue in the group, he seemed very disturbed. A further diagnostic study confirmed the conclusion that the boy was psychopathic. Because of his inability to develop a relation with the case worker, he was later closed in the casework department as well.

Another boy on whom we shall report briefly is Jerry. He came for treatment at the age of eleven. The school had reported that he had been troublesome since the very beginning. The mother was said to be a weak person, unstable and nervous, who had no control over the child. She granted all his wishes and pampered him. The father was a bully who got into serious difficulties with the law. The boy was described by the mother as disobedient, beyond her control, and given to temper tantrums. When interviewed by the present writer toward the end of the treatment of the boy in an effort to have him placed in an institution, she was very protective of her son, minimized his problems and assured us that he would get over his difficulties as he grew older. The same had been the case with one of her sister's children, she said.

The following is one of the curious episodes in the history of this boy: Jerry was a voracious eater and at as early an age as five or six, would rise during the night and eat all the food he could find in the house. He made it a practise of eating, among other things, all the sugar that happened to be in the sugar bowl. As a disciplinary measure, the father once placed a quantity of salt in the bowl instead of sugar. Jerry ate the salt without a whimper or complaint.

When Jerry was in 4A, at about ten years of age, he held up a number of younger children for pennies in the school yard. He did some petty stealing in the school. There was a history of stealing since the boy had been five years old. At the age of twelve, he stole the contents of a teacher's purse and used the money for movies, had photographs taken of himself, bought goodies and concealed the remainder of the funds on a window sill in his home. The teacher also reported missing stamps. The school complained that he molested little girls and annoyed other pupils as well.

Individual treatment was ineffective, and we accepted him for exclusive group treatment. Jerry also was absent but five times out of sixty-eight sessions. Three of these absences were due to illness.

Contrary to the picture presented by Bernard, Jerry was at first industrious and at the beginning displayed considerable interest in clay modeling. He later developed interest in airplane building. At the group, he would become restless after a half hour's work and would then become extremely annoying. This he did by teasing, passing sarcastic and caustic remarks, but more frequently by wrestling with the boys. When he got into real difficulty and was threatened, he hid behind the therapist and appealed for protection. But these threats did not deter him from his habitual behavior. He continued gaining what seemed to be real satisfaction from abusing and intimidating the boys.

Jerry seemed to feel in his element only when engaged in such destructive and annoying activities. He used to contrive every imaginable means to encourage the other boys, particularly Ziggy, a very weak boy, to give chase. This continued for several months. After this, he became generally noisy and boisterous, threw around chairs, started free-for-all fights and shouted and yelled. One of the characteristics observed was that he was easily affected by the group atmosphere. When the boys became boisterous or aggressive he at once joined in. On occasion, however, when there was a real lull and quiet in the group, Jerry would for a while, at least, become subdued, but would soon initiate some disturbance. The report on Jerry stated that he definitely showed delinquent trends from the very beginning. He took home anything he wished from the group, including projects upon which other boys worked.

Not being too clear as to the meaning of this behavior, the therapist did nothing to stop him. After four months of this, Jerry began to ask permission to take materials from the group. He also asked the therapist for money in amounts ranging from ten cents to a quarter. This was given him. Although he promised to return the money he borrowed, he never did. He then began demanding such items as stamp albums, stamps, and games. After a period of several months, we decided to limit Jerry's self-indulgence and restrict him. When he asked for money, it was refused him. At this, however, Jerry did not show any irritation or disappointment. One of the interesting observations was that despite these requests, Jerry seldom looked directly at the therapist and kept his distance.

In the following year, we transferred Jerry to a group of boys three years older than himself. We felt that the control the older boys would exercise upon him might be beneficial. Faced by a situation he could not master, as he did in the previous group, Jerry brought a friend to support him with whom he formed a separate unit within the group. To break this up, his friend was placed in another group as a regular member, though he was not a client in the agency. When he was left alone to face the group of older boys, Jerry withdrew into himself, and worked continuously all alone; but he began to steal. The therapist was aware of it, and faced him once or twice with it. Jerry usually gave some indifferent excuse, such as: "I thought that it was all right for me to take these things," or "I was going to ask your permission." However, when he committed an act of serious vandalism against the building and stole rather costly appurtenances, the other boys became aware of Jerry's stealing. It was then necessary to close the case, which also taught us the lesson that a child of this character cannot be reached by the permissive environment in Activity Group Therapy.

Both boys reported on in this chapter seemed to have defective superego development. In both instances the fathers were either narcissistic or punitive persons, while the mothers were over-tolerant and over-indulgent. There was little opportunity to introject the paternal image which forms later in life the inhibitive mechanism against impulsive behavior. In both cases there was narcissistic attachment to the self, probably encouraged by the mothers' over-indulgence and emotionalism. The permissiveness of the group reinforced these narcissistic trends.

Our conclusions are confirmed by a recent study on the effect of "group psychotherapy of a permissive nature" on neuropsychiatric battle casualties.[4] The Minnesota Multiphase Personality

⁴ Rashkis, Lt. Harold A., and Major Donald A. Shaskan: The Effects of Group Psychotherapy on Personality Inventory Scores, *Amer. J. Orthopsych.* April, 1946.

Inventory was administered by the authors to twenty-two patients before and after intensive group treatment of six weeks. The results are given by them in the following table:

Significant Deviations in 22 Cases

Personality Factor	Before Treatment	After Treatment	Per cent change
Hypochrondriasis	9	5	−44
Depression	13	6	−54
Hysteria	10	5	−50
Psychopathic deviate	10	10	0
Masculinity-femininity	6	4	−33
Paranoia	6	3	−50
Psychasthenia	8	4	−50
Schizophrenia	8	6	−25
Hypomania	9	13	+44

It can be seen from the above that no change occurred in the psychopathic deviate, while the greatest change was effected in the factor of depression (from 92 to 51 on the Minnesota Multiphase Personality Inventory). The latter observation, too, is confirmed by our experience with Group Therapy. Margolis has also found no change in children with psychopathic personalities.[5]

It would seem that if there is any treatment at all possible for such individuals, it would have to begin at a level where early introjection of parental authority in the formation of the superego occurs. The psychopath acts impulsively, and he is subject entirely to the authority of his own narcissistic, instinctual drives. A permissive therapy group cannot supply the authority he requires; he rejects authority. Having no anxiety concerning behavior, there is no way of reaching basic impulses.

We have had no experience with psychopathic personalities in interview groups. Our interview groups consist mainly of neurotic patients. However, we had experience with one psychopathic adult in such an interview group and we found that after

[5] See table p. 39.

he had given reign to his aggressive and narcissistic needs orally, he left the group. He was not able, nor did he wish, to withstand possible retaliation to his behavior on the part of the others.

Because of the inability of the psychopath to relate to a therapist, it is, at least theoretically, conceivable that such patients cannot be treated individually either; certainly not in the beginning phases of therapy. The approach to them would have to be a less personal one, requiring no transference relation. This would indicate a group, but the group has to be of an authoritarian nature such as institutions provide. In a setting where the group meets only at stated periods, the psychopath can readily escape the consequences of his acts by simply not coming to the meetings. An institution does not offer such an easy escape. Restraints, inhibitions and punishments are applied consistently. Instinctual fear is aroused, and the authority symbols that should have been established earlier in life are now supplied by the institution and its staff. The total setting is of such nature that one has to find some way of adjusting to it in order to survive.[6]

It is our opinion that Group Therapy in a clinical setting is unsuitable for psychopaths. Their treatment must come from the pressure of a planned authoritarian environment, which the patient cannot evade, and which arouses in him primary fears.

---

[6] For a further discussion of institutional treatment of psychopathic personalities, see Slavson, S. R.: An Elementaristic Approach to the Understanding and Treatment of Delinquency, *Nerv. Child,* October, 1947.

Chapter Six

TREATMENT OF A CASE OF BEHAVIOR DISORDER THROUGH ACTIVITY GROUP THERAPY

Attention is directed here to the treatment of one boy by Activity Group Therapy. The material is so organized as to illustrate some of the dynamics paramount in this type of treatment. Besides the elements and dynamics described in preceding chapters, special emphasis is given here to demonstrating some additional factors in the process. Among these are the *supportive ego* [1] and the progressive choice of such a supportive ego. By this is meant that the child attaches himself in the group to members that meet a basic need within himself. As some of his personality difficulties are overcome and he feels stronger, he attaches himself to other, more adequate members in the group. This is one of the very important dynamics in Activity Group Therapy.

Another dynamic illustrated by the record material in this chapter is that of *critical events*. By these are meant the situations that assume special meaning because of their relation to the central problem of the patient. During treatment, each member of the group is exposed to, and participates in, many experiences. Some of these are more important than others. Events that touch basic problems are most "critical" in the treatment process. Thus, when a child who is afraid of aggression comes in direct conflict with another member of the group, the event becomes a critical one for him. If he fails in this, his difficulties may be intensified. If he masters it, his fears are allayed. Though the above is an over-simplification of the actual dynamics, it illustrates what is meant by it.

[1] For an explanation of the terms used here, see Slavson, S. R.: *An Introduction to Group Therapy*, New York Commonwealth Fund, 1943.

The material presented also demonstrates how *frustration tolerance* is increased. Because of the strengthening of the ego, the subsequent more hopeful attitude toward the self and the improvement in self-evaluation, the child is able to withstand frustration more successfully than he had been in the past.

The dynamic of *libido-binding activity* also emerges from the treatment history of the boy in this chapter. From a distractible child, unable to focus his attention on any job, he developed into an individual strong and integrated enough to concentrate on and finish the projects he undertakes.

The emergence of a *primary group code* also becomes clear here, for we see how a flexible group organization gradually arises, which later results in definite rules and regulations. Thus, a group of *social mobility,* characteristic of therapy groups, moves toward becoming one of *social fixity,* which is the structure of the ordinary group formation. [2]

Murray Berman was brought to the Jewish Board of Guardians by his mother, in April 1937, on the suggestion of a case worker who was treating one of Murray's older sisters. Murray was ten-and-a-half years of age at the time, had an I.Q. of 80, and was in the 5A school grade.

Concern about Murray's behavior had prompted Mrs. Berman to bring him to the agency; she hoped also that he would be sent to camp. The problem as she stated it at first was that Murray was shy, that he was unable to defend himself if beaten by other boys and that "it wouldn't do him any harm to come to the J.B.G., and besides, he wanted to come." Other problems that were later revealed were enuresis, lying, failure at school, inability to fulfill parents' aims, feelings of rejection by parents, inability to get along with boys, and severe sibling rivalry, especially with the next younger brother, age eight.

Murray expressed bewilderment at the inconsistent treatment by his mother, who alternately petted and beat him. The father intimidated and beat the boy. As a result of all this, Murray was confused as to his status in the family.

[2] See Chapter One, p. 26.

The family consisted of the father, age forty-seven, the mother, age thirty-two, two girls, ages nineteen and sixteen-and-a-half, two younger brothers, ages eight and five, and a baby girl, age one-and-a-half. The father was a W.P.A. worker. The two older girls were Murray's half-sisters, their mother having been Mrs. Berman's sister. Murray's mother married her brother-in-law upon the death of her sister. Mrs. Berman felt that there was a stigma attached to being a "second" wife and impressed upon the entire family that this must be kept a secret. Consequently a pattern of secretiveness seemed to permeate the family. Mrs. Berman was quite defensive about Murray. She withheld information about his developmental history and other data. When questions were put to her, she quickly changed the subject.

The boy was treated in the case work department from April, 1937, to January, 1938, and the case worker found him emotionally inaccessible. In a summary on the client, the referring worker stated:

"Contact with the boy reveals a very fearful, withdrawn youngster with conflicts about his lack of aggression, his relationship to his mother and his rivalry with his younger sibling. He seemed unable to respond with spontaneous feeling to the case work relationship." The case was therefore transferred to the Group Therapy department January 1938, and the boy placed in a therapy group.

One of the outstanding facts in the history of this case which must have had an important bearing on this boy's disturbance was the mother's role in the family and in particular her attitude toward this first child of her own. The mother felt guilty toward her dead sister and was ashamed for having profited through her sister's death to the extent of getting the latter's husband for herself. Her first child by this marriage therefore had to represent a living symbol of her offence against her dead sister. She at times petted and at others beat him.

Murray's history revealed emotional deprivation in his childhood in a number of areas. He had been inhibited and he suffered from a deflated ego. What an activity group could do for him, was:

1. Supply consistency in relationships;
2. Release blockings to spontaneous self-expression;
3. Help overcome feelings of impotence and weakness through association with stronger and more outgoing boys;
4. Provide a consistent and constructive relation with a male adult;
5. Supply a field for working through sibling relationships on a more wholesome and more satisfying basis than he had an opportunity to do in his own family;
6. Give him security with boys through a permissive group with a low social pressure by virtue of which he would be able to act out his repressed aggressions without fear of retaliation, punishment or criticism;
7. As a result of all this the boy's ego would be strengthened, so that he would change his perception of himself as a weak, worthless person.

Murray was invited by letter to join a group. He responded to the first invitation and attended his first meeting [3] on January 16, 1938. In four years of group treatment, of a total of 142 sessions, he was present at 138 and absent from four. He attended *all* meetings the second year.

At the first meeting, only one other boy besides Murray was present. Although at first he did not recall where they had met, he realized later that it had been at camp. Murray painted a boat on a piece of board but said he thought it was not good. He showed little interest in the material and equipment and spent most of his time wandering around the room. He asked the other boy present to play a game, but had to play with the therapist because Edward was interested in working with arts and crafts. Murray was attracted by an electric jig-saw, but did nothing constructive. He wanted to know if there would be more boys in the group and was told there would be.

When it was time to leave, Murray asked if he could stay longer

[3] "Meeting" throughout this chapter refers to "group treatment session."

but was informed that the room was available for a specified time only and was used by others when the group left.

The striking quality of the boy's behavior at this meeting was his aimlessness, his inability to focus attention, his inability to be productive or to finish anything he started, and his belittlement of his own capacities.

Murray was absent from the second meeting. He came forty-five minutes early to the third meeting. He said he could not come the previous week because he was "bad" and his parents punished him by forbidding his attendance at the "club." He did not reveal why he was punished. He also told the therapist he had visited Edward since the first meeting he had attended.

Again, at this meeting, Murray asked the therapist if more boys were coming and was told that more were expected. When two new members arrived, Murray asked the therapist to play a game with him. The therapist invited the new members to play too, and soon Murray was playing with them alone when the therapist said he had something special to do.

A trip to the museum had been planned for this meeting. When the therapist put on his coat, one of the boys who was painting asked him to wait. Murray also wanted to continue working. While the group was waiting, Murray took out a piece of plywood, brandished it in the air, attempting to break it, and said, referring to himself: "A man of steel." Then he bent it in half and Nathan, one of the new boys, helped him break the wood in two. Murray then took out the electric stylus and said he was going to print "Home, Sweet Home" on one of the pieces of wood, just as Edward had done two weeks ago. Murray printed a few letters, and left his work unfinished. He then took a piece of paper, held the electric stylus to it and watched it burn through the paper.

While the therapist was putting the materials away, Edward took a rope and tied it around Murray, and as Edward held one end, Murray playfully galloped around the room.

Murray told the boys about the fifteen cents his father gave him and offered to treat them. They refused. Throughout the trip, Murray was very active and playful as he ran around sometimes teasing and annoying the other boys, sometimes aping passers-by. On the train, he declared himself to be Tarzan and with Edward swung from the straps. Throughout the subway ride, Murray and Edward were together. Murray was mischievous all the way to the museum. He pointed to a house and said it looked like a gangster's den. While waiting for the train, Murray told the therapist he did not expect to be promoted although his father had promised him a dollar if he were promoted to the 6B. He attributed his school difficulties to the fact that his family had moved during the term and he had to change schools. When the boy had to go to the washroom in the museum, he insisted that the therapist go with him because he was afraid of getting lost. While viewing the exhibit, Murray kept grabbing whatever he wanted to see from the other boys. With Edward as support, he objected to leaving the museum when the therapist suggested it was time to go. The therapist promised that they would come back some other time.

On the way out, Murray said he wanted to eat in the Automat and elaborated on the process of putting in nickels and taking out food. In the Automat, he spent the fifteen cents the therapist gave him and each of the other boys. He then asked the therapist for an additional five cents, which was given him.

On the way home, Murray was as boisterous as on the way to the museum. He raced through the streets shouting and fighting with the boys. He fought with Edward, who seemed to be annoyed with him, and kept hitting Murray. Then he began to direct his aggression against the other boys.

The fourth meeting found Murray at the electric jig-saw, but now he was not just playing with it. He cut out objects he had traced on wood. He seemed to find it necessary to explain his poor tracings by saying that his hand was shaky because he was nervous. While working with the jig-saw, he would open the meeting room door so that people in the hallway could see him at work and admire him. He showed a momentary interest in leather work when he saw the therapist make a key-case, but he could not follow through this interest. In contrast to the other members, Murray always insisted upon the therapist's approval before he did anything. He told the therapist that his father had told him always to ask for permission. When the therapist indicated that members were free to make what they wanted to, Murray said: "You know, you're a nice man." He made a picture for the therapist and gave it to him.

Because of the consistently constructive attitude of the therapist, we found Murray becoming attached to him and expressing his positive feelings towards him. This is analogous to a "positive transference" in psychoanalysis. Since we were dealing here with a behavior disorder, however, the important step toward improvement was made—namely, the boy was establishing a relationship. Since the chief difficulty in behavior disorders occurs usually in this area, his positive statement concerning the therapist was rather important. We shall see later that he acted out also his negative, hostile feelings against the therapist, even though he did it in a veiled way—attacking the other members of the group, disturbing the group atmosphere and making demands on the therapist.

As the meetings progressed, Murray was becoming one of the most active members in the group. He requested more outings, became more friendly with some of the boys and expressed hostility towards authority through playful attacks on Edward, who was now the group bully. Murray played with fire even more frequently. He burned holes in pieces of plywood with the electric stylus. The therapist encouraged this interest in fire by providing cans of sterno and an asbestos pad. Murray coined nicknames for some of the boys, which could be interpreted as a form of provocation to be attacked. As he became more involved with the boys, he was less helpful with group chores. This seemed to be especially true at the meetings when Edward was present. Murray seemed attracted to Edward, who was a strong, robust, very masculine boy—everything Murray wished to be. He played with him and was now also visiting Edward at his home.

At the eighth meeting, Murray noticed two boys on the floor, fighting and wrestling. Enviously, he said to the therapist: "Gee, look at all the fun they're having." The group visited the Metropolitan Museum of Art that afternoon. Murray was shocked at the nakedness of statues and the exposed genitals. He was the only member of the group who was embarrassed by the nude statues, and held on tightly to the therapist's arm throughout the visit.

Although friendly with new boys, he seemed to resent their presence. When arguments arose, he always sided with the older members. His excessive interest in food now found a new expression. He assumed the responsibility of preparing the food and setting the table.

At the thirteenth meeting, Murray said that he would like to make a bracelet for his mother. At about this time, he also remarked that he was fighting back when the boys at school hit him.

In the weeks that followed, the therapist noted that Murray's interest span was still limited and that only occasionally did he finish the work he began. Although he was still annoying to the group by his uncontrolled, disorganized manner of play and behavior, he was much quieter. He still seemed fearful of physical injury and hesitated before getting into fights or quarrels. Murray's fantasy of being a "Tarzan" continued as did his playing with fire.

Murray came to the seventeenth meeting, but only after he had done his homework five times. This, he explained, was his father's method of punishment if he did not get his homework perfect. That afternoon, Murray said to the therapist that he first became friendly with Edward when an arts-and-crafts leader of a group in a settlement house they used to attend treated Edward roughly, and Murray said he pitied him.

As on several previous occasions, Murray went to call for Edward when Edward did not appear at the nineteenth meeting. On the train to the park, Murray offered the therapist some chocolate, which he said he got from a vending machine by blowing into the coin slot. He said that Edward had taught him how to do it. In the park, Murray made a whip which he struck against the trees as he passed. He said he would like to hit somebody " 'til their body looked as if it was sunburned." During this trip, it became apparent that Murray was seeking Edward's support in the group, but that Edward did not need Murray's support. Edward made this quite evident with the result that Murray began to associate more closely with Robert. Murray later referred to Edward as a "louse."

At the twentieth meeting, Murray again related his father's rigid discipline for incorrect school homework. He spent most of his time wandering around the meeting room in a rather aimless manner. He suddenly jumped on a table, raised his left arm and said loudly: "I'm Hitler." (This same incident was repeated two weeks later.) Up to this time, Murray's impulsive use of vulgar language seemed to embarrass him. He would always apologize, explaining that he always used slang when he felt irritated. He told the therapist that this was his birthday. The therapist arranged a party in his honor and, for this occasion, purchased more food than usual. Still desiring to cling to the therapist when walking in the street, Murray referred to Sidney and Irving as "louses" because they were holding onto the therapist's arms. However, Murray got his share of attention at the swimming pool, at the next meeting, when he constantly called to the therapist to watch him dive.

June 30, 1938, the twenty-third meeting for Murray and the last meeting of the first year, we found Murray fighting back and defending himself in a fight with the boys. When a few boys tried to dislodge him from his seat next to the therapist, he fought back and was quite adamant in his refusal to give up. This was really the first time Murray struck back and defended himself physically. At the meetings, he was still playing with the electric jig-saw a good deal of the time.

When the group was adjourned for the summer vacation, Murray wrote to the therapist, telling him how much he missed him and how anxious he was for the club to start meeting again.

It may be helpful to evaluate the progress Murray made in the first six months of activity group treatment.

There is evidence that Murray had what we designate as "social hunger." He desired to be with other children and even though his relationships were not as yet of a constructive and positive nature, there was a need on his part to be with them. We note that at the first few meetings, when there were only a few present, he asked whether there would be more boys in the group. He then attached himself first to Edward and then to Robert, indicating a craving to have friends. This need usually originates in early childhood where the capacity to relate to people is first conditioned. Despite the present social pathology at home, there seemed to have been, early in his life, opportunities for more positive relationships.

A patient who has a need for other people, presents a good prognosis in Group Therapy. Here, he has an opportunity to satisfy his inner cravings and through relationships, to correct his attitudes and feelings toward people. A child with this craving is also ready to give up some of his undesirable behavior and attitudes in return for the acceptance that he receives from others.

In the beginning, Murray was faltering, inconsistent, unproductive. His impotence was obvious when he barely gathered courage to make a feeble attempt to produce something. He apologized for his shaky hands. His inability to use his hands was another indication of his impotence and perhaps reflected a repressed masturbatory conflict. As this aspect of his difficulty emerged, there were clearer indications of sexual anxiety. He displayed an exaggerated reaction, in the museum, to the nudes with exposed genitals, and his fascination with fire bcame more and more manifest.

In the permissive environment of the therapy group, and in the presence of a consistent, understanding adult, Murray was able to express, without fear, his compensatory fantasies of strength and power. He is "a man of steel," "Tarzan," and "Hitler," with limitless power. Activity Group Therapy utilizes this striving for strength and power; i.e., the latent strength of the personality, as a positive element in the treatment. It addresses itself to the pathology of the client and aims at strengthening the positive elements of the personality. In this process, it is necessary to give the child an opportunity to relate his fantasies to reality. This, as we shall see in later parts of the report, Murray did.

The greatest strides that Murray had made so far were in overcoming his fears of aggressions. At first, he submitted by galloping like a horse driven by Edward. He then used nicknames for some of the boys. He actually verbalized his envy of the two boys who were having fun wrestling and later, in place of his primary feeling of impotence there emerged a pattern of exaggerated and destructive potency, envy of other boys, passive disobedience toward the therapist, with an attendant increasing rebellion against authority, particularly symbolized by his defiance of the group bully, Edward. This was further demonstrated by his increasing use of vulgar language and by his impulse to beat someone until his body looked as if it were sunburned. This hostility was directed specifically against Edward, but symbolically may have been intended for the punishing parent figure in his family, perhaps his father, who had been beating him, and by transference, also for the therapist. At the last meeting of the year, the twenty-third, he resisted efforts of other boys to dislodge him from the seat near the therapist. Thus, we see that the security which he gained from the support by the therapist and by the other boys helped him overcome the fear of his hostility and aggression. In this growth the therapist's role is important. We see how Murray sought his support at various times, walked with and clung to him, gradually absorbing, as it were, strength from the adult.

Another factor that generated the strength necessary to express aggression was the support he received from other members in the group. Murray attached himself to Edward, who was the bully. Through identification with Edward, he perceived himself to be strong and felt secure because Edward, who was the strongest in the group, supported him. This function we designate as "supportive ego." However, as Murray felt himself stronger, he abandoned Edward for a more normally behaved boy, Robert, and rejected Edward's previous support by calling him "louse." This progress from one supportive ego to another is an integral part of the therapy in a group.

The characteristic of the supportive ego is that it is temporary and serves the immediate needs of a child. As soon as he sloughs off the particular problem for which the supportive ego serves, the child drops his supportive ego and moves on to another that serves him in the next step of growth. This is a common observation. Without this movement, there would be stagnation, for growth occurs through constantly widening relationships that serve the expanding needs of a child.

One other tendency is worth noting, namely, that the dependence on the therapist which had had a regressive quality up to this time, began to reflect a growing recognition of difference between the attributes of the therapist and the qualities of his own father. He began to see the therapist as a good parent.

A related tendency, which also deserves attention, was his need to confess to the adult his urge to steal; for example, to get chewing gum illegally by blowing into the slot machine. This confession of guilt connected with submerged, prohibited cravings was an important part of the process of gradual resolution of this boy's anxieties.

When the group resumed meetings, September 18, 1938, with the same therapist, Murray again responded to the first letter and attended all the sessions. One of the boys gave the therapist a New Year's greeting card. Murray apologized for not having sent the therapist a card but the therapist said he knew all the boys wished him a Happy New Year, whether they expressed it by card or verbally.

While rowing on Crotona Park Lake, Murray teased the boys by rocking the boat, and interfering with the others. When walking in the street, Murray still held on to the therapist's arm. Again, Murray began to play with fire, which he had abandoned toward the end of last Spring. He threw lighted matches into a bottle of mucilage. When he used up all his matches, he asked the therapist for money with which to buy more matches. This was given him. Murray became more demanding of the therapist, making increasing requests for money to buy things for himself, such as wheels for his skates, and to buy a shoe shine box with which he wanted to earn money. The therapist explained that the money could be used only for club purposes. Murray agreed that it would not be fair to the other members if he took money for personal use. At a later meeting, he wanted to save empty soda bottles so that he could keep the deposit money, which he was not allowed to do.

Murray began now to sell shopping bags in the market to earn some extra money for himself. When the group had to wait for Murray to bring the bags home before going on a trip to the Planetarium, he invited the therapist and the boys up to his house. The boys declined the invitation, and Murray soon returned with some fruit for them. He offered some to the therapist, while his entire family waved to him from the window. He also gave the therapist half of the candy he had bought.

When one of the boys who had bought refreshments for the group left some change on the table, Murray pocketed one of the coins. There was a mischievous look on his face as he did this. However, he returned the coin to the therapist when another boy called the latter's attention to what Murray had done.

Murray's interest in work with materials seemed to be growing. He talked enthusiastically about the airplane model he had made and said he was going to make another one the following week. This was the first time such enthusiasm was evidenced by Murray about any of the work he had done.

At the twenty-ninth meeting, when the other boys had expressed a desire to go swimming, Murray suggested that the group go bicycling. He acceded to the wishes of the majority, however.

At this period, Murray displayed an intense interest in money. He would refuse to spend the money given him by the therapist to purchase refreshments on trips. Sometimes, he would spend only part of it. At other times, the sight of the other boys enjoying their food was too much of a temptation, and he would spend his money as well. It was noticed that after meetings, the boy tried to keep money received upon the return of empty soda bottles. He would give it up only when asked for it. Murray also made attempts to appropriate for himself work done by other boys in the group. He once saw an airplane kit that belonged to another boy and had been left out of the cabinet accidentally. Murray picked it up and said: "This is mine." The therapist said: "You know, for a moment I thought it looked like Seymour's." Murray grinned and said: "I guess it isn't mine after all." On one occasion, when Murray took a paddle and said he made it, Robert said that the paddle belonged to him. Murray at once returned the paddle.

At the thirty-second meeting, Murray asked if he could take home with him the Monopoly game so that he could play with his brother. The therapist said that other clubs used the same room and equipment and might want to use it. Murray retorted that he would bring it back early. When it was suggested that he ask the other boys, and his request was denied, Murray did not seem disturbed by it.

When a trip to the Metropolitan Museum of Art was planned, Murray objected, but came along nevertheless. This time, he smiled mischievously at the statues of nudes. Again, he asked if he could keep the money given him for refreshments. The therapist told him that he would have to ask permission of the group. The group denied this permission. At this period, Murray's interest in playing with fire was rapidly diminishing, but he was now borrowing materials and tools to take home. His span of concentration in working with materials had greatly increased, and he used to complete the work he undertook.

At one meeting he hid the leather punch under his jacket where the therapist could not see it. He approached the latter and said: "I'm taking it home." The therapist smiled but said nothing, whereupon Murray returned it to the closet. At this meeting, Murray made a bookcase, painted it and left it to dry.

The first evidence of direct aggression came out at the next meeting, the thirty-eighth, when he and Edward had a fight. Edward struck Murray and ran away. Murray attacked Edward, raining blows on his body until he sank to the floor. Murray said he hoped he had taught Edward "a lesson."

At the fortieth meeting, Murray for the first time actually asked one of the other members, Jack, to wrestle with him.

During the following weeks the boy's interest in work with crafts materials continued. He had taken to working with linoleum and although he discarded what he had made, he continued trying to improve his work. The figures he drew were of men smoking cigarettes.

At the forty-third meeting, Febuary 5, 1939, Murray's developing aggressiveness led to a wrestling match with Edward, the boy who terrorized most of the other members of the group by his bullying manner. Murray did not yield until he was actually overpowered by Edward.

At school, Murray was taking shop work and was quite enthusiastic about it. He was making good grades. At the group, Murray devoted much more time to playing ping-pong with the boys and was now the best player in the group. Another interest he developed was bicycle riding. He undertook to make inquiries at the local stores about renting bicycles. When he learned that the cost was more than the group had anticipated, he suggested that all forego refreshments so that the group could hire bicycles.

The poor cooperation on the part of the boys in cleaning up the room after the meeting led to a brief informal discussion at the close of the fifty-second session. The therapist asked the boys for suggestions and Murray suggested that the therapist punish those who did not cooperate, though he was often guilty of it himself.

Murray was now attacking Edward more frequently and wrestled with him.

Murray's behavior at the table was among the best in the group. He helped clean up the meeting room and was rather well behaved when the group was eating. At the last meeting of the season, he asked the therapist to spend more money than usual at this time, because it was the last meeting. The therapist explained that his money was limited and much as he would like to do it, he could not. Murray accepted this limitation, without protest.

At this point, we see that certan trends displayed earlier have become crystallized. This boy now showed less preoccupation with food, less need for indulgence from the therapist on an immature dependent basis. With the subsidence of his interest in food and demands for other infantile indulgence, he discovered his increased capacities.

It is of interest to see that the boy at this stage placed an increasing emphasis on money, similarly as he did earlier on food. First, the sole source of money was the therapist, and he was completely dependent upon the therapist for it. He therefore "chiseled" as much as he could. Gradually, as his dependent attitude subsided, he began to realize that it was possible for him to earn money. There are many possible interpretations of this transition. The simplest and safest implication is that money represents a kind of power, the power to accomplish gratification of needs through one's own productive efforts. In the beginning, he seemed to feel that he had no such resources within his own person and was therefore forced to exploit the therapist's resources of money. Later, he seemed to discover that he had that power within his own person when he began to earn money. There was therefore less need to wheedle money from the therapist.

The symbolic content of the temptation to steal is of considerable interest here. It is possible that the stealing represents, in part, a reaction to the experience of emotional privation by his mother, and in part, an effort to gratify certain of his repressed sexual cravings. This aspect of his temptation may link up his preoccupation with fire, with enuresis and perhaps with masturbation. The disguised content of his love feeling for his mother was in no way revealed but is a consideration to be borne in mind.

Another aspect of his attempts to steal represents clearly his urge to steal credit for the masculine competence of the other boys. His own feeling of inadequacy was amply demonstrated in many ways. He reacted to it by trying to steal the adequacy of the other boys. Gradually, however, his feeling of inadequacy diminished. In fact, the gradual diminution of his weakness in the area of masculinity seemed to run parallel with the increasing freedom with which he confessed to the therapist his temptation to steal. In this connection, it is important to note the effect on the boy of the therapist's good-natured, tolerant attitude toward the confession of his urge to steal.

Simultaneously, there was an irregular continuation of his need to impose infantile demands for indulgence on the therapist. The intensity of this need varied from time to time in accordance with his anxiety, in particular with his fear of competitive aggression, and his fear of his own destructive urges. With his growing strength, and increased self-evaluation, his infantile, regressive behavior diminished. On the lake, for example, he rocked the boat and annoyed the boys. However, as the meetings progressed, this type of infantile provocativeness disappeared. He redirected some of his aggression to working with materials and creating things. This could be characterized as constructive aggression as against the infantile or destructive aggression in children. We can assume that when Murray began to make airplanes and other objects, and rode a bicycle, his aggressiveness was taking on more mature forms. Another part of his aggressive impulses was spent on direct combat with the boys, and still another was sublimated in games such as ping-pong and the like.

The most important single development during this period of treatment was the increase in *frustration tolerance*. Repeatedly, the therapist and the boys denied Murray's requests. He accepted these denials without becoming disturbed, irritated or hostile. He also acquiesced to the group's decisions on trips, contrary to his own desires. The ability to accept frustration is one of the most certain tests of an integrated personality and real maturity. We know from his history that Murray had not been able in the past to accept limitations without manifest or covert disturbance.

Another major development that we observed during this year was his improved relation with his family. He now had sufficient assurance to invite the group to his home. We also note the more positive attitudes of the family toward Murray. They gave him fruit for the boys and the entire family waved good-bye to him from the window. In the previous year, Murray had made a bracelet for his mother. In this second year, he made a number of useful objects for the home, including a large book case. Apparently, he now was accepted and his status had become both clearer and stronger. This must have had great value in building up Murray's ego. He no longer was confused as to his relationships. He felt more comfortable and happier, therefore he no longer needed to attack the world or activate its rejection of himself. As the image of himself became more positive, he did not need to resort to subversive or negative means to focus attention upon himself by destructive or infantile means.

Also here the function of the therapist should be noted. During the first year, he had given Murray whatever he asked for. This year, the therapist had limited the boy. In other words, Murray was no longer an infant in the nurture or pre-oedipal phase of life. He was now a child ready for some discipline. His growth was manifested by his reasonable statement when the therapist refused him money: "I guess it wouldn't be fair to the other boys." The readiness with which he admitted that the airplane kit was not his when the therapist said that it looked like Seymour's, was another indication of Murray's growing maturity and his capacity to accept frustrations. We also observe that this year Murray did not attach himself to anyone in particular, but moved toward the group as a whole. He became a part of the social setting.

We have already indicated elsewhere that as patients become more certain of themselves, they give up attachments to individual supportive egos and are able, because of their growing self-confidence and strength, to integrate with the group as such. In fact, we observed that Murray in his inner need to throw off his old self and his dependence, on frequent occasions now attacked Edward, the bully, quite violently.

To give the boy a further opportunity for growth, he was transferred to a new group and a different therapist in the fall. He knew a few of the members of this new group and quickly became chummy with them. Since the new therapist and some of the members were not acquainted with the meeting room, Murray volunteered to show them its set-up and facilities.

A trip was planned for the first meeting. Some of the boys wanted to go bicycling. Together with a few other members, Murray was opposed to this because of the expense involved. This was quite in contrast to the demands made by Murray in the first two years of treatment. The group did go out bicycling.

The following week, Murray said that Edward had come for the trip after the group had left and referred to him as "a trouble maker." On another occasion, Edward forced his way between Murray and another boy in the therapist's car. Murray at once got out, went to the front seat and said: "I don't want to sit near him."

Murray, who by now had learned to ride a bicycle well, was very enthusiastic about this activity. At the fifty-seventh meeting, Murray asked permission to take a ride by himself near his home, apparently to show off to his family and friends. Murray repeated this at the next bicycle trip, and taught one of the new boys to ride.

At the following meeting, a new boy, Herbert, was added to the group. Herbert spoke well and had scientific interests that attracted Edward. Murray at first resented this intrusion, but whereas he usually patterned his work after Edward's he now began to definitely ally himself with other members in the group. When Edward wanted to go off on his own once, Murray calmly said: "It's better if everybody does the same thing, or you'll break up the club."

He frequently played ping-pong and when he made a pair of wooden sandals, he exclaimed: "Gee, they came out nice, didn't they? It's the first good thing I've made here." And when the boys stopped grabbing food, he expressed satisfaction with the orderliness. In contrast to his own demeanor earlier, Murray expressed embarrassment in public with Edward's loud and noisy behavior.

Murray gradually began to make contact with Herbert, the scientifically-minded boy, whom he had resented at first. His first contact with him was when Murray asked him to show him how to draw a side view of a racing auto for the model he was making.

When Charles, the boy whom Murray taught to ride a bicycle, failed to come to the next bicycle trip, Murray asked permission to call for him the moment he received his own bicycle. In a short while, Murray came riding back on his bicycle and Charles running along on the sidewalk towards the bicycle store. Murray again visited on his bicycle the block where he lived.

Having experienced some success in wood work by making wooden clogs, Murray decided to make a book case. He said: "My mother wants me to make a book case for the house," and seemed very gratified when another member of the group copied it. He worked a month on this project and later announced happily: "This is exactly what my mother wanted."

Murray now helped other boys with their work and helped put things away after the sessions. When he wanted to abandon his boat model for an airplane model the therapist suggested that he finish the boat model first. Murray remarked: "I think you're right, it's better to finish one thing first," and gave his airplane model to another boy. He worked on his model for six consecutive sessions, and the boys admired it. One of them said: "Gee, you've got a dandy model. I wish I had yours;" to which Murray replied, embarrassed: "Go on, yours is even better."

At this time, too, Murray preferred having refreshments in the meeting room to visiting restaurants.

The use of profane language by some of the boys in the group seemed to upset Murray, although he, himself, had used bad language before. He attempted to curb this habit of the boys. He also became quite solicitous about the boys in the group. For example, when one of the boys took sick in an ice cream parlor, Murray took care of him. Once, he brought a baseball so the group could go to a park to play ball.

Murray's attitude toward school was also becoming more positive. He contributed the models he made in the group to the school exhibits. He said he was complimented by a number of the teachers on his work.

The boy became much more articulate, acted in a mature manner and showed less need of the therapist. He was deriving greater satisfactions now directly from the group itself where he was forming increasingly stronger relationships. Towards the end of the third year, one of the boys said to the worker: "Murray's a swell guy. I like him best of all."

Under the date of June 3, 1940, towards the close of the third year of treatment, when Murray was thirteen years old, a home visit was made. Mrs. Berman told the case worker she felt that Murray's progress and good adjustment was directly due to the influence of the club.

Ordinarily, only very few clients are carried beyond the second year, but because Murray came to us with a specially weak ego and intense feeling of helplessness, we felt that an additional year of treatment was indicated.

At the end of the third year, we were not certain still that Murray would be able to make a transition to the community. He was therefore retained in the group. In addition, Murray reached the stage in development where his membership in a group would be of value to other boys. The presence of one or two fairly normal children in a group helps the therapeutic process of the more disturbed, and Murray could be helpful in this situation.

To test the maturity and ego strength of a child, and to expand his experience with people and groups, we always transfer children to groups other than the one in which they have made first contact. Usually, this can be done after the first year.

The ease with which Murray made this adaptation to his new group, mirrored the progress he had made. He became chummy with the boys and easily transferred from one therapist to another. He became a sort of guide for the group, since he knew the building better than the others. His identification with the group, as contrasted with his need for individual support, was clearly indicated by his satisfaction with the orderliness in management of its affairs, by being economical with the agency's money, his annoyance with Edward's boisterous behavior on trips, which reflected upon the prestige and the dignity of the group. He even gave up a bicycle trip because, to use his words, he "didn't want to break up the club."

His readjustment in the family setting was further revealed. He again took his bicycle to show his family that he could ride by himself, and on several occasions his mother asked him to make objects for the home. The acceptance in the group and in the family was reflected in his own acceptance of himself. He now could accept praise, which made him anxious before. What is even more significant was that he volunteered the statement that the object he made was good.

Children with a weak ego and devaluated self-esteem are afraid of the obligation of living up to praise and are even more afraid of being successful. Murray's perception of inner power and his self-acceptance were further confirmed by the fact that he helped and taught others bicycle riding and doing crafts.

The shift in association was another confirmation of his changed self-evaluation. He dropped the inferior Edward and tied up with Herbert, whose I. Q. was 165, and whose scientific and literary knowledge was way beyond his years. Herbert did not serve as *ego-support*. He was Murray's *ego-ideal*.

We further note that the boy spent much time in playing ping-pong, badminton and similar active games. These are *releasing activities* as differentiated from painting and wood-working, which are, to varying degrees, *immobilizing activities*.

Fearful children isolate themselves from the impact of the group by engaging in individual occupations. The more secure can participate in the more aggressive group games. Murray moved from *isolating occupations* [4] to a definitely *activating game* like ping-pong. This activation occurred both within himself and in relation to other children.

All three therapists in whose groups Murray was a member reported the great value of bicycle riding to Murray. The activation of power and the sexual connotation of riding a bicycle are of great value to boys of Murray's character. At this point, Murray, through his physical activity and bicycle riding, displayed increased masculine adequacy. He asserted himself more effectively. He now defended himself in aggressive encounters; he showed expanded initiative and greater productivity. His aggressive energies were no longer paralyzed.

He displayed to his mother his new-found power and was gratified by her approval. He evidently modelled himself after the group therapist, as a symbol of an effective male figure. Murray modelled his conscience as well as his self-control after him. This put him on an equal plane with his father (therapist).

His neurotic temptation to steal had entirely disappeared. It is evident that a potential predelinquent trend based on neurotic motivation was in the process of being dissolved.

---

[4] See Slavson, S. R.: *An Introduction to Group Therapy*, loc. cit., p. 191.

The last year of treatment, 1940-41, Murray was placed in a *transitional group*,[5] the purpose of which was to prepare its members for transfer to a regular settlement house club. It will therefore be noted that as the year progressed, the level of functioning had been constantly raised to approximate more normal group life.

In this group, Murray had a third therapist, who now acted as a leader of a social club. He found Murray outgoing and at ease with himself and the boys. Murray was purposeful, active and cooperative. He still reacted with irritation to coarse language, but less violently. He participated actively in group discussions, voiced his opinions fully and spoke of his camp experience. He helped with chores and did most of his work on his own. He submitted to restrictions easily and accepted limitations without complaint. Once, when several of the boys, including Murray, began to push each other around the room using chairs as lances, they were told that they could not abuse the furnishings of the room or would not be permitted the use of it. Murray stopped at once, without any indication of perturbability.

He no longer wandered aimlessly as he used to and when others raced around the room, Murray stopped them, even though this meant laying himself open to a fight with Jerry, a very tough boy. Once, when the boys dawdled, the therapist announced there would be no refreshments. The boys were at first surprised and asked if they could eat alone. The leader replied: "If we hadn't spent so much time cleaning up, we would have had plenty of time for refreshments and you can settle this amongst yourselves, but I cannot give you any money. The office doesn't permit me to give you any money." This was their first experience in group frustration.

Murray's ability to accept all kinds of frustrations from the leader and the boys was quite noticeable. When the group decided against him, which occurred frequently, he did not become aggressive. When a swimming party was planned, the leader explained that the cost being high, the group would have to go without refreshments. Murray's reaction was: "O.K., then

[5] *ibid.*, p. 326.

that means we don't have any refreshments, that's all."

Murray played actively and showed proficiency in such games as improvised hockey, paddle tennis and ping-pong. He expressed enthusiasm about the school he was attending and also expressed a desire to be a doctor.

After thirteen sessions of the transitional group and in view of this progress, it was decided that Murray was no longer in need of a protective therapy group and he was transferred to the settlement house. Arrangements were made for a member of the settlement house staff to invite the entire group to visit. The boys responded with enthusiasm and suggested that they join as a club.

By pre-arrangement, the boys were shown the available facilities. Murray repeatedly asked: "Will we get into here as a club? Do you think we'll be able to get house cards here?" After the tour around the building, the boys met in one of the meeting rooms for the remainder of the evening. The boys were enthusiastic about the prospects of having a regular club. Murray asked: "How about paying dues? Suppose we have a treasury?" It was through his efforts that a club was set up with officers. Murray was elected treasurer. He participated actively in setting up rules and achieved a real triumph when tough Jerry said: "These are Murray's ideas, and we ought to thank him for his help." He functioned conscientiously as treasurer and his suggestion, at a later meeting, of having blue and scarlet as club colors was accepted. At one of the meetings, when Jimmy was particularly noisy and disturbing, Murray changed chairs with another boy to be near Jimmy and control him. Murray was elected the representative of the club to a club convention. He was later elected captain of the club team.

At a later meeting, one of the members suggested: "Why not go back to J.B.G., we can get more and get other things, too." He referred to the money for refreshments, trips and crafts materials, which they no longer had now. Murray was among the boys who said: "We're happy here. We like it. You can go back if you want to."

Gradually, Murray joined individually some of the activities in the settlement on evenings other than the club meeting. At Murray's suggestion, the club decided to alternate weeks, so that the boys could spend more time in activities available on the particular evening when the group met.

After this experience as a member of a regular club, Murray was transferred to the settlement. In the closing summary, it was noted that Murray now gave no indications of the difficulties described at the time when he was originally referred. He was described as being accepting of, and accepted by, children; he was getting along well at school and at home.

A visit to the home revealed that Mrs. Berman felt Murray had improved. She said that Murray loved school now, that he had very nice friends, and that she was satisfied with his general development. She felt that the club helped "develop his personality."

The latter part of the case history speaks for itself. It is clear that the boy now adapted to new situations with expanded emotional flexibility and with confidence in the adequacy of his performance. He changed from the role of an inhibited frightened follower to the role of a more or less secure, but benevolent, leader. It is apparent that he took with him into these new situations the social and moral standards that he acquired in the group, personified originally by the ideals and mores inherent in the personality of the therapist, but now representing a part of this boy's own personality. In entering these new situations, he perpetuated the *esprit de corps* of the original group. This new-found constructiveness in his social attitudes, together with a sense of real competence had largely displaced the earlier patterns of passive destructiveness and inhibited aggressive drives. The potential delinquent tendencies suggested in his impulse to steal seemed to have disappeared from the picture. The anxiety related to sexual disturbances was no longer apparent and with this the enuresis and the preoccupation with fire disappeared. The fear of bodily injury was no longer present either.

It should be noted also that his personal aspirations now assumed a socially desirable form. More concretely, and of great importance was that the boy was happier, capable of greatly increased initiative and of real emotional spontaneity, and that he participated energetically and successfully in social relationships.

In terms of process in Activity Group Therapy, we must note that the group as a whole is being adjusted gradually to a new situation. In the course of this adjustment it is denied all the privileges it enjoyed before, such as food, materials, carfare, and trips. The members at this stage have to assume the relationships and the functioning characteristic of a social club and whatever opportunities they wish to enjoy they must create themselves. They also become a part of a larger community.

The frustration of the group takes various forms, as exemplified by the fact that when the boys become obstreperous the leader directly tells them they must stop; this is not done in the earlier stages of treatment. When the tools are not put away and the room is not cleaned properly, the leader calls attention to the fact and conveys his expectation for greater responsibility. Gradation of the leader's own assertiveness toward the children and his setting of standards is important and must occur some time in the treatment process. This is the *principle of graded reality*.[6]

We recognize that reality is a relative and changing concept. It has a different meaning to different persons and different meanings to the same person at different stages of development. The importance of timing of authority cannot possibly be exaggerated for any type of therapy, particularly in a group, for reactions of a group are more infectious and threatening than they can possibly be in individual treatment.

As we review this case, we are impressed with the fact that Group Therapy has met the child's needs through consistency in relationships with an adult and children, release of spontaneity, overcoming the feeling of weakness and impotence, the opportunity to work out sibling relationships on a more constructive basis, and most of all it served to change the image of the self from a weak and impotent person to one adequate to deal with his own impulses and the pressures of the environment.

[6] See also Slavson, S. R.: Differential Methods of Group Therapy in Relation to Age Levels. *Nerv. Child,* April, 1945.

Part III

INTERVIEW GROUP THERAPY

Chapter Seven

INTERVIEW GROUP PSYCHOTHERAPY WITH PSYCHONEUROTIC ADULTS [1]

It is axiomatic that any form of psychotherapy for the neuroses must accommodate itself specifically to the unique imbalance of emotional forces that characterize the neurotic state involved. The corrective techniques must be systematically pointed to the conflict patterns which must be resolved to make way for a healthier adaptation. The only specific therapy for the neuroses so far widely recognized is psychoanalysis. If one attempts to apply group treatment to the neuroses, one is obliged to demonstrate tangibly how this method can benefit them. Some efforts in this direction have been made by Paul Schilder, Louis Wender and Alexander Wolf. [2]

Since the term, psychoneurosis, is used in a variety of ways, it is perhaps best at the outset that the term, as it is used here, be defined. It has been often said that a psychosis constitutes a denial of outer reality, and a neurosis represents a denial of inner reality while allegiance to outer reality is preserved. This

[1] For a general outline of Interview Group Therapy see Chapters One and Ten as well as parts of subsequent chapters.

[2] Alexander Wolf has made effective use of group psychotherapy for the neuroses in private practice; an account of his experiences came to me through private communication.

Paul Schilder: The Analysis of Ideology as a Psychotherapeutic Method, especially in Group Treatment, *Amer. J. Psych.* November, 1936; *Psychotherapy*, New York, W. W. Norton and Co. Inc. 1938, pp. 157-159, 197-255; Results and Problems of Group Psychotherapy in Severe Neuroses, *Mental Hygiene*, January, 1939; Introductory Remarks on Groups, *J. Soc. Psychol.* August, 1940; Social Organization and Psychotherapy, *Amer. J. Orthopsych.* October, 1940.

Louis Wender: Dynamics of Group Psychotherapy and Its Application, *J. Nerv. Ment. Dis.* July, 1936; Group Psychotherapy; A Study of Its Application, *Psychiat. Quart.* October, 1940.

is a striking description of neurosis, but it is not entirely accurate. It is not possible to deny inner reality without to some extent distorting external reality as well. The reality sense in neurotic persons is always impaired to some degree. The focal symptoms of a neurosis are anxiety and inhibition resulting from conflict. The anxiety is sometimes diffuse, but more often manifested in specific symptoms. The central characteristic of a neurosis is the presence of an unresolved conflict between prohibited underlying tendencies (erotic or destructive) and conscience. The presence of excessive guilt feelings and fear of punishment impair the sense of pleasure and cause chronic insecurity. The buried impulses are displaced, disguised, and find vicarious release in symptomatic behavior. There is a self-protective effort to wall off the disturbance within the area of symptom behavior, somewhat in the same way as pus is walled off in an abscess. The symptom usually incorporates within its structure: (1) a symbolic representation of a buried urge, (2) the need for punishment, (3) the ego reaction to the conflict, and (4) a varying amount of secondary emotional exploitation of the neurotic suffering.

Besides this, certain other changes take place in the personality. The emotional capacity for close, satisfying human ties is impaired. Neurotic persons cannot commit themselves fully to personal relationships, since they fear they must pay too high a price in suffering or renunciation. In consequence, the whole process of social maturation is retarded. In addition there is a weakening of aggressive powers, a lack of confidence, a fear of failure, a defective ability to deal with new situations, and a discrepancy between aspirations and actual achievement. Thus, such individuals always show some degree of deficiency in the total adaptive functions in addition to the disability that results from specific symptom formation.

The therapeutic aims in employing the group method with the neuroses are the following:

(1) To provide emotional support through group relationships.

(2) To activate emotional release in the area of specific anxiety-ridden conflicts; in particular, to encourage the release of

pent-up aggression. This process entails the utilization of group psychological influences for the selective re-enforcement of some emotional trends and involves the suppression or dilution of others.

(3) To reduce guilt and anxiety, especially through the universalization of common forms of conflict.

(4) To provide opportunity for the testing of various forms of social reality as personified in individual members of the group or in the group as a whole.

(5) To provide opportunity for the modification of the concept of the self in the direction of increased self-esteem and recognition of constructive capacities. This in turn tends to increase the acceptance of other persons and tolerance for frustrating experience.

(6) To foster the development of insight arising from an actual living out of emotional drives in the context of the multiple relationships within the group. Interpretation is employed only when the expression of specific emotional trends has been sufficiently solidified.

In order to demonstrate in a concrete manner the effects of the group experience on neurotic conditions, a condensed summary of six sequential therapeutic sessions will be presented. It must be kept in mind that a completely convincing record of the therapeutic process in a group can be presented only through the medium of talking moving pictures, which would record all the subtlety of varying facial expressions, vocal inflections, gestures, and other physical movements. It is obvious that a purely verbal description inevitably loses some of the most significant nuances of the psychological phenomena in group treatment.

For the purpose of demonstrating the proceedings and of illustrating group interactions and their value, the experience of one neurotic patient will be high-lighted in this chapter.

John was thirty-four years of age. His illness had begun some ten years ago following the death of his father by suicide. This shocking episode precipitated a deep change in the patient's whole personality: he brooded over his father's suicide and felt depressed for three years. He had a feeling of emptiness in his stomach, was morose, irritable, and worried. He had developed numerous symptoms among which were insomnia, and fear of crowds, of dirt, and of heights. He engaged in chronic self-reproach and had a compulsion to re-check everything he did. He suffered also from somatic disturbances such as generalized weakness, dizziness, palpitations and diarrhea.

Before the time of his father's suicide, John had led what he considered a normal existence. He had not been nervous. He and his father had been close companions and the father had been very indulgent with John who, in turn, was extremely dependent upon his father and leaned upon him for all decisions. He had felt much closer to his father than to his mother or sister. His father had been quite wealthy, but shortly before his death had suffered financial reverses. The family was thus impoverished and the patient was forced to assume the role of provider. Before this time, he described his state as follows: "I didn't have a care in the world, I got everything I needed from my father."

Session I. John reproached another member of the group for having absented himself without informing the physician. This was a characteristic gesture of respect for authority. He began by saying: "Group therapy helps you realize that there are others who have the same problems, and it makes you feel less alone." He then described his symptoms and his sufferings. The therapist asked him why he had to constantly check up on himself. John answered this question by telling of a terrific rage he had had against his sister. He said: "I lost my head and smashed a coffee cup. She took a muffin I wanted for breakfast. I worry a lot. I'm not sure of myself. I can't concentrate. I can't sleep. After an attack of Vincent's Angina [3] five years ago, I thought I was going to die. I thought I caught it from a girl. It was a murderous kiss."

At this point he veered off to the question of his job. He had held it seven years and intended to keep it because his boss was tolerant of his peculiar behavior. Whenever he felt anxious, he

[3] Vincent's Angina is a diphtheroid angina.

jumped up and left the office. He felt there were not many bosses who would allow that. Other members chimed in, advising John to keep his job because it was a "cinch". John remarked that at one time he had hoped to make a million dollars a year, but he now knew that this hope was fantastic. Although he had a college degree, he was now resigned to starting at the bottom of the ladder as a shipping clerk. He had always tried to do things perfectly, for his own satisfaction. He vigorously told Bill, another group member, that you have to be willing to start at the bottom and not start with any high-flown ambitions. He preached to Bill that his trouble was that he did not want to work at all. Bill replied: "I don't want a job, I want a future."

The therapist commented that Bill had the habit apparently to begin doing something but actually stalled in order to make someone else do it for him. He was not interested in work as such, but really wanted an insurance policy for the future; he wanted someone to take care of him. Further discussion revealed that Bill had no regular earnings but depended on his wife's salary. John remarked, with a sharp show of envy: "I wish I had a wife to support me." Bill described how he defeated his own purposes, how he had lost all hope and had completely resigned himself to failure. He said: "My father used to tell me the best thing for me would be to be shoved back where I came from and be made all over again."

The therapist pointed a remark at John, who seemed to prefer talking of Bill's failures rather than of his own. The therapist said, among other things: "This is a case of the lame and the halt leading the blind. You, too, feel you're a failure." As in reaction to this, John was stimulated to confess more of his personal difficulties, his checking up on himself constantly and his having to keep his feelings locked within himself. He was unmarried and, since his father's death, had lived with his mother, for whose support he was responsible. He said: "For this reason I can't marry, except if the girl has a good job." He described his relationship with his father. He was tremendously shocked and dazed by his father's suicide. He said: "It was not like father and son. We were like two pals." He had never fully recovered from the shock of his father's death. His father had been indulgent, but had taught him the necessity for work. His mother had been shocked, too. She had developed hyper-thyroidism, high blood pressure, and later had to have an operation. Both John and his mother had been ill since his father's death. He had many of his mother's symptoms.

He was usually depressed in the morning, often upset by bad dreams. He related one of these: "I fell in a trap and wanted to run, but my feet were glued. I felt paralyzed and woke up in a cold sweat." He had had this dream repeatedly in childhood. The therapist remarked: "The danger seemed right on top of you." To which John replied, "Yes," and added that in this mood he was irritable and did not want people anywhere near him.

In the latter part of this session, another member took the center of the stage and discussed a dream in which he walked about dressed as a woman. Further discussion linked this dream with this man's habitual provocative and exhibitionistic behavior. John was stimulated by this recital: he teased and accused the man of being conceited and showy. At this point all members of the group had become dramatically excited and tried hard to show each other up. This was clearly a contagious defensive response, indicative of repressed "homosexual anxiety" (fear of attack) in all of them.

In a characteristic manner John was ingratiating in his initial contact with a man in authority. He chastised another member of the group for being disrespectful of the psychiatrist's authority. He attempted also to disarm the psychiatrist of any possible hostility to himself by elaborating on the subject of his physical suffering. This signified at once his self-punishment and his wish for protection. At this point the therapist tried to penetrate the disguise of the patient's hostilities by challenging him on his need to constantly check on himself. John gave a clear answer to this challenge, namely, that he needed to check up on himself in order to control his suppressed rage. He gave an instance of this violent rage against his sister. He then quickly shifted from this to relating an experience of infectious illness, seemingly the result of his having kissed a girl. Here the punishment was obviously linked with the theme of sexual transgression and, significantly enough, connected associatively with an assault upon his sister. Immediately after this he reverted to the problem of his relationship with older men. He evidently became extremely dependent upon employers who took care of him and forgave him his "peculiarity," which actually represented his concealed rage.

In the sharp interaction with other members, John saw in bold relief some of his own tendencies, namely his extreme dependence, his wish to be cared for, and his resentment of exertion. His envy of another man, who was supported by his wife, was unmistakable. He saw also that his guilt feeling did not allow such self-indulgence. He therefore preached to other members against yielding to such temptations. At this point the therapist actively interpreted to the patient his preaching role. He induced him to confess his feeling of failure, his fear of marriage because of his own wish for the dependent, protected position. John described how his father had indulged him, how he felt guilty about it, how he and his mother were shocked in a similar way by his father's suicide, both having the same physical symptoms and neither having recovered. He then reported a dream in which he was trapped in a position of danger, was paralyzed, and unable to escape. One might conjecture that this dream reflected his fear of being caught and punished by his father. This account stimulated another member to present a dream of himself as a woman; a sequence of events that stimulated in John and in other members of the group an anxious feeling of being exposed to attack. They responded to this anxiety with excitement and a defensive urge to attack each other. John's guilt and his feeling of being exposed to bodily injury were deliberately not linked by interpretation in this session.

Session II. In this hour John described other symptoms: fatigue, upset stomach, sweating, pounding in his chest, numbness, pain in his arm. He made a suggestion to the group that the doctor not be called a psychiatrist; he resented the use of the term "psychiatrist." In his mind the use of the term "psychiatrist" was like "syphilis." He could talk much more easily if he could regard the doctor simply "as one of the boys." He associated the word "psychiatrist" with bars. It made him feel locked up. He resented the emphasis on the difference between the doctor and himself. He resented social barriers.

Another member disagreed, insisting that there was an actual difference and, if one recognized the doctor as a superior person, a more important person, one could get more out of him. The therapist interpreted this to John as a desire to feel closer, even equal; and as a feeling of being menaced by conceiving of the doctor as in a superior, authoritative position, whereas the other member welcomed his feeling of inferiority in order to get more out of the doctor. The therapist suggested that if, on the other hand, John had felt superior to the doctor, it would actually make him feel guilty and fearful.

John went on to say that he checked up on everything he did to make sure he did not do wrong. He amplified his fear of failure. "I go through what I call a thousand deaths a day through fear. I get exhausted. I sweat, my heart pounds, my pulse races. I feel I am dying and I get terribly irritated. I am afraid of the boss. I try to be perfect because I am afraid he is going to bawl me out. I am afraid that I might leave the gas jet on, so I check up on myself. This fear makes me urinate frequently. I get thirsty. My tongue gets dry and I drink a lot and have to urinate more. I get tongue-tied with the boss. I am afraid I might say the wrong thing. I have the impulse to curse. I feel guilty all the time."

The therapist remarked that because of his guilt feeling John had to pay in suffering for his hostile feeling to the boss. John confirmed this comment with a story. At fifteen years of age he had caught his elbow in a door. He had experienced severe pain but had returned again and again to put his elbow back in the door. He felt drawn to do it repeatedly; he wanted to see how much pain he could take. He was afraid of heights, yet he felt drawn to them. John went on to say that at the age of nineteen or twenty, he had a tonsillectomy and the anesthesia had not taken. He had a feeling of choking. In dreams he felt trapped and choked. He was fascinated by situations in which he experienced pain or in which he suffered in other ways. The therapist remarked that he seemed to enjoy the attention he got when he displayed all of his sufferings. Perhaps he felt that the therapist would be kinder to him than the boss was because he suffered so much, and also, by evincing so much punishment of himself, he would avoid punishment by the therapist.

Once again the patient had started out with an effort to disarm the therapist of hostility to himself by complaining of his suffering. Immediately afterward he proceeded to try to strip the psychiatrist of his professional authority, seeking to make his own position safer by making the psychiatrist "one of the boys." He explained this by confessing his fear of the psychiatrist and his feeling that the difference between them made him feel locked up. This was reminiscent of the dream he had reported in the previous session in which he had been trapped and paralyzed and unable to protect himself against anticipated assault. John interacted with other members who felt differently about this issue and not menaced by the psychiatrist's position. The therapist took occasion here to bring into focus John's guilt as the basis of his fear of the psychiatrist. John proceeded to validate this interpretation by confessing his conviction that he always did the wrong thing, by which he meant that he had to struggle constantly to control violent feelings against his superiors. In consequence he had an intense fear of retaliation; his anxiety became translated into somatic manifestations and fears of death.

The therapist made a clear-cut interpretation at this point to the effect that his physical suffering was his way of paying for his aggressive feeling against the boss. John affirmed this by giving an example of an actual experience, wherein he had inflicted pain upon himself. He linked this trend associatively with experiences of surgical operations, which had evoked in him the fear of being killed. The therapist made a further interpretation that if John punished himself by his physical suffering he hoped that the boss would then be kind rather than hostile and injurious.

SESSION III. Other members of the group held the center of the stage and, for a time, John was pushed into the background. He injected himself into the discussions, attempting to interpret the meaning of other members' problems. For example, he disagreed with one man by saying that it was no solution to run away from one's problems, to escape to a farm because one disliked people. He interpreted the desire of another man to evade responsibility for his wife. At the same time, he admitted to difficulties of his own. He said he felt better but still suffered from sweating, diarrhea, and rapid pulse. If anyone made a mistake at work, he said, he got angry and grumbled. Often he simply left the office and ate something. No matter who made the mistake, he felt responsible for it. He had thoughts of falling from a high place and killing himself, but usually stopped such thoughts at the point where he was falling out of the window. He did everything fast: talked fast, ate fast, walked fast; in fact, he raced with himself. He was not able to calm down or relax.

The patient again indulged in some preaching to other members of the group. He held that escaping one's problems was no solution. Here he seemed to identify his own tendency to evade responsibility, and glided once more from this to a preoccupation with his own suffering which represented self-blame and self-punishment.

SESSION IV. In this session John reminded another member that he should respect the doctor and avoid offending him. A third member talked about his depression, his feelings of tension when with people, and his urge to scream when in a crowd. John said he had a similar impulse to flee from crowds. The therapist interpreted this as his fear of losing control over his violent impulses against people. John again talked of his inability to assert himself with the boss, his feeling of paralysis when in the presence of any authority, his intense fear of disapproval, his compulsion to be obedient and ingratiating. He felt completely under his employer's control. He was afraid for his own life. Getting the boss' approval was much more important than getting a raise.

However, it was John himself who insisted on being perfect. He criticized himself constantly and felt guilty all the time. He was afraid that if anything went wrong he would be blamed. The therapist remarked that perhaps he felt guilty about many small things in order to hide his real crime. John responded by recalling a childhood memory: at five years of age he had taken some money out of his father's penny bank. (His father had symbolized an inexhaustible source of money.) Thereupon, his father had given him the worst licking of his life. He never stole after that. He had learned his lesson well.

John said he did not understand why, but he was always building up a fantastic story in order to get a girl to feel sorry for him. At this moment he was staring at the therapist's secretary who was a good-looking woman. John wanted to be sure that a girl would not rebuff him, but he did not really want the girl. Another member advised him to be more aggressive. John went on to say that he felt obligated to the boss because he had helped him to take care of his debts. He was always afraid to ask the boss for anything. At the same time, inside himself, he wished he could "show the boss up." "The whole thing is a fight, a continuous battle within myself."

Other members described their own emotional conflicts. One told of his fear of being caught in situations from which he might not be able to escape. Another told of how he could help others build up their lives but could not help himself. John said of this last man that he built himself up and knocked himself down repeatedly, that he got panicky in the middle of doing something, that he puffed himself up too big, got scared by what he had done, and retreated from the situation.

Again the patient started out with his usual ingratiation through reproaching another member for a disrespectful attitude toward the therapist. John then experienced together with another member the fear of losing control over his suppressed rage. He linked this with his feeling of paralysis and with his compulsive obedience. The therapist interpreted John's readiness to blame himself and to confess small offenses as a device for hiding the real basis for his guilt. John responded by recalling a child-hood memory in which his father beat him severely for having stolen money. John then shifted his interest to the therapist's secretary, as though unconsciously desirous of stealing this wom-an's attentions from the therapist. He did so, however, in a way that would inevitably end in the defeat of his wish. Another member sensed that he had not really intended to succeed in this competitive effort and advised John to be more aggressive. John then discussed his ambivalent feeling toward his boss which involved dependence, on the one hand, and resentment of obedi-ence on the other. Various members of the group indicated how they trapped and defeated themselves, a tendency that John also displayed. John saw his own self-defeatist tendencies re-flected in the personalities of the other members and, in partic-ular, his tendency to retreat when he became fearful of his own aggressiveness.

In this session for the first time John's aggressiveness was ex-pressed in the form of competition with the therapist for a woman's favor.

Session V. A new member joined the group who was in the same line of business as John's father had been. The new patient said he did millinery designing, but was starving to death. He said all the men and women in his family were millinery design-ers. There was some discussion of competition with women which was described as "tough." The discussion turned to the suicide of John's father. The men questioned him concerning it. John's father had been very wealthy but had lost heavily on the stock market, and had then begun to draw heavily on his $250,000 insurance. On the day he had committed suicide, he had taken a bottle of whisky with him. John feared whisky. It always made him depressed and reminded him of his father's suicide. He did not blame the liquor, but thought it had helped. He got pleasure out of talking of morbid things; he wanted to get them off his chest. When the policeman stood at the door of his house to inform him of his father's death, John inwardly knew that his father had committed suicide even before the policeman opened his mouth to speak.

Another member hinted that John wanted his father to die in order to collect the insurance. The others laughed. John quickly perceived the implied accusation, but said his father and he had been pals and his father had been very indulgent, even to the extent of taking him to a speakeasy and letting him take out one of his own models. One member of the group pointed out to John that even though he had felt convinced his father would kill himself he had done nothing to stop him. John said he had thought of keeping a close watch on his father, but actually had not done so.

His father had felt very guilty for having withdrawn the insurance money to the detriment of the family; he had even cried. John had fantasied that his father would jump under a train. Another man interjected the remark: "So you could get the insurance money?" The member who had accused John of wanting his father to die, confessed that his one big ambition was to have money. John said that he had had many fantasies of his father's death before it actually happened, explaining this as a pleasure in having morbid thoughts, for he had experienced pleasure in the thought of his father's dying. By way of further explanation he said he was extremely worried. He did not have the confidence that he could take his father's place and support his mother. Another member said that he would much rather hold on to his father than have the insurance money, because his father might recoup his losses and make another fortune: a father might actually be worth more alive than dead.

This session made dramatically clear the patient's death wish for his father and his consequent guilt. Another member of the group accused John of having wanted his father to die so that he might collect the insurance money. John at first made a weak attempt to deny the truth of this accusation, but seemed to accept it by confessing his pleasure in having had morbid thoughts of his father's death before it had actually taken place. John expressed his ambivalence about his father's death in his feeling of inability to fit into his father's shoes and assume responsibility for the support of his mother. In this session it was noteworthy that the group members themselves carried the momentum of the therapeutic activity. They channeled the direction of release and did their own interpreting. There was little active intervention by the therapist.

SESSION VI. In this session John again receded into the background as the problems of other members became the center of attention. John was strongly annoyed because another member absorbed the attention not only of the therapist but of the whole group, and he reacted by tormenting this other member. They argued, and then, to some extent, analyzed the content of their argument. John was annoyed because this member tried to impress people by his showiness, whereas he himself tried to impress people by his humility. While he was teasing him, John said: "I would probably play with him and then kill him, but after that I would miss him." He confessed to irritation because this fellow simply did not want to work for a living. There was some discussion of the obvious envy reaction involved and of the connotations of John's fantasy of killing this member of the group and afterwards missing his company. Some parallelisms were drawn between this ambivalent attitude and John's feeling toward his father.

Here again the patient dramatized his envy of another man who seemed less guilty about his dependent tendencies and was able to indulge himself more than John's own conscience would allow him to do. Toward this man John displayed the same ambivalent emotions that he had shown in regard to his father.

In reviewing this case we find that the salient symptoms of this patient were anxiety, hysterical conversions, obsessive-compulsive traits, and psychosomatic disorders. He had fears of bodily injury and of death. Both his sexual and his aggressive drives were inhibited; he showed psychic impotence, and he was conscious of being a weak man. He had desires for a woman but tended to disown them because of his guilt and fear. His heterosexual urges were concealed behind defensive cruelty and a fear of damaging any woman he might possess. He degraded women and at the same time competed with them. He showed a tendency to regress from oedipal conflicts to earlier levels of psychosexual adaptation. Toward men he had a passive homosexual attitude, but displayed a violent ambivalence, alternating attitudes of flirtatiousness, submissiveness and ingratiation with attitudes of violent hostility. He carried on an incessant struggle to control his destructive, assaultive impulses. The death wish against his father was a central phenomenon. He had excessive guilt feelings and a need to suffer, as well as a need to inflict pain on others. His suffering was exploited secondarily for exhibitionistic purposes.

It is necessary to discern just how this neurotic behavior was received in the group and dealt with by the group method.

The patient attached himself strongly to the group and attended all sessions faithfully. To be accepted by the group was an important experience for him; the group represented a family. Of special significance was his need for a close bond with men. He used the therapist and the group as continuous sources of kindness and emotional support. He established a strong transference on a dependent basis; but his aggressiveness easily revealed itself behind his passivity. He erected an image of the therapist as a strong father, and of other members as weak fathers. Toward the therapist he was mainly submissive, ingratiating, and careful to avoid offense; toward the other members he was at times flirtatious or fawning, at other times provocative or sadistically overbearing; still at other times silently contemptuous. At first, not daring to challenge the paternal authority of the therapist, he displaced the hostile aspect of his ambivalence on to other members, evidently because he conceived them as weaker than the therapist, and so was less afraid of retaliation from them. In this way he hoped magically to preserve the strong father's support and approval. Later he became more openly aggressive against the therapist, and his murderous destructiveness was only thinly veiled. He also identified the other members with himself, attacking and disparaging them instead of attacking himself. He exposed their weaknesses and failures instead of his own. This provided a rich therapeutic opportunity to penetrate to and strip the patient of his defenses and rationalizations. These appeared as resistance to revealing the real unconscious source of his anxieties hidden behind a compulsive camouflage of aggression and an effort to deny sexual desire, particularly in the context of the therapist's relationship with his attractive secretary.

It was evident that group interaction exposed the significant neurotic conflicts of the patient. The patients activated in each other release of repressed feelings surrounding their central conflicts. The therapist exploited group pressures to guide the direction of release and, when emotional trends became ripe, he engaged in active interpretation. In this connection it should be noted that often spontaneous interpretations offered by other members rendered unnecessary such activity by the therapist.

On the cathartic level the experience promoted a release of pent-up feelings. This occurred in the group interaction through which the discharge of emotion was not simply on the verbal, but rather on the more primitive action-level. The most notable illustrations of the patient's neurotic "acting out" were his flirtations with other members, his tendency to humiliate them, and the dramatization of his death wish against another member, identified with his father.

The emergence of anxiety was plainly visible in connection with the dramatization of his conflict patterns. The central conflict, and the one which generated the greatest anxiety, was his need to possess a love object completely, to force gratification of his passive wishes for love, protection, childish indulgence, and then to destroy that person. As these conflicts were expressed and the corresponding defenses and rationalizations removed piecemeal, the anxiety and guilt appeared and could be relieved. In this phase of the process it was not the therapist exclusively but all the members of the group who interpreted the real basis of his fears. Insight, therefore, was acquired by this patient in a context of an actual social experience. There was a significant impact between unconscious drives and interpersonal reality, as personified by the therapist, some other members, and the group as a whole. Certain irrationalities were clearly exposed in the interpersonal contacts within the group. It was possible to direct the group experience so as to utilize this situation for continuously correcting the patient's distorted perceptions of the attitudes and motives of others toward him. It should be added, for purposes of caution, that the maximum therapeutic effect is achieved only after the significant problems are "worked through" repeatedly in many sessions.

The manner in which neurotic disturbances can be favorably influenced by a group experience was demonstrated in these six sessions. John shared anxiety-laden experiences with other patients of the group. He saw in them, as in a mirror, the reflection of his own neurotic trends. He saw anxiety reactions to suppressed rage, to fear of losing control, to feelings of inadequacy and failure as a man, to fears of bodily injury sustained through the assault of a punishing parent figure. In the relationships within the group, both with other members and with the therapist, he lived out his dependent patterns and his resentment of obedience. He expressed his aggressive feelings against persons in authority more and more openly. The sources of his guilt were laid bare by interpretation. He exposed to the group and to the therapist his worst side, and found it tolerated and understood. As a result, he derived emotional support and increased strength as a person. Through releasing his aggressive feelings without evoking the kind of rebuff and punishment that the fixed emotional patterns of the past had led him to anticipate, he felt more accepted and more powerful. This provided a background in which his image of himself could gradually become constructively modified. As his guilt and his feeling of unworthiness diminished, he could restore his sense of self-esteem and lessen his feeling of having been irreparably injured.

The group situation is one in which interpersonal patterns are actually "lived out," not merely verbalized; this is highly significant since it is commonly known that release on a motor level is far more effective therapeutically than the more superficial verbal release. It should be borne in mind, however, that the degree of "acting out" is continuously controlled by the directing influence of the therapist, and thus can be prevented from jeopardizing the unity of the group and the therapeutic goal.

In the group situation a tangible social reality is always present. The patient's contact with it is immediate and inescapable. The therapeutic process moves back and forth between this social reality and the patient's inner emotional life. This supplies a basis for a continuous impact of the patient's images of interpersonal relations upon their actual nature as perceived and interpreted in the group interactions. It would seem to be a form of psychotherapy operating both "from inside outward" and "from outside inward", contrasting somewhat with traditional psychoanalytic therapy, which is mainly a therapy operating "from inside outward."

In the analytic situation the neurotic patient is insecure. He is unable to pursue pleasure or success without anxiety. He fears the irrational and destructive elements in his impulse life. He vacillates: at one time he may side with his impulses and fight his conscience, at another time he may ally with his conscience against his impulses. In any case, he can release these impulses only in the context of some form of interpersonal reality, but he is confused concerning the validity of his social reactions, and in his personal values and concepts of reality. Fundamentally, he is confused in his image of himself, and is therefore never clear as to his exact role with other persons. Consequently, he gropes blindly in an effort to test the suitability of his reactions. Unsure of his own standards, he seeks to rely on the presumably more valid, safer reality standards of the analyst. He seeks to organize his impulses and in particular his hostilities in relation to the analyst's concepts of reality. In essence, this is a process in which the patient temporarily borrows the analyst's ego orientation to bolster his own security. On the other hand, the analyst is loathe to interfere with the patient's spontaneous effort to resolve his conflict. He, therefore, maintains a relatively neutral position and tries to avoid, as far as possible, imposing his own reality standards. But all the while it is a part of the analyst's role to personify reality for the patient, not only in the context of the therapeutic relationship but in that of the whole outer world as well.

The analyst is a symbol of reality, but actually there is no tangible social reality (group pattern) in the analytic relationship. This produces something of a dilemma. In actual practice it is most difficult to carry out satisfactorily the analyst's role as the representative of social reality. This is at once the most complex and yet most responsible aspect of his function which is rendered even more delicate by the realization that there is an ineradicable subjective component in every person's definition of reality. In this sense, concepts of reality, interpersonal values, patterns of integration of primitive drives and, finally, concepts of a co-ordinated self, tend to remain in an unresolved state in analysis for a long time.

Thus, in psychoanalysis we have a type of experience in which the inhibiting effects of reality and conscience are deliberately and specifically minimized in order to free the expression of repressed urges; that is, the analyst plays a role that causes the menacing aspects of reality and moral restraint to recede so that the patient may feel safer in the realization of unexpressed needs. Yet there remains the paradox of the analyst's having continuously to represent social reality. In the larger sense this is predominantly a therapy "from inside outward."

Group psychotherapy functions somewhat differently: it seems to operate in both directions. In contrast to the analytic situation, a tangible social reality is always present in a group in the form of dominant aims, ideas, values, and interpersonal patterns. The patient's contact with this tangible social reality is immediate and inescapable, and the therapeutic process moves back and forth between this social reality and the emotional life of each individual patient.

From these considerations a significant speculation arises. It is common knowledge that even those patients who have had a successful analysis seem to experience some amount of confusion and often a considerable lag in effective social readjustment in the immediate post-analytic period. This is entirely logical, since the patient uses this period to re-orient his ego-patterns to his newly achieved insights. Often, however, such patients experience a real distress in their efforts to translate the analytic understanding into new and more constructive forms of social experience. One is tempted to wonder in this connection if group psychotherapy would not be a valuable supplement to psychoanalytic treatment as a bridge between the newly structured insights and the establishment of new forms of interpersonal relationships.

The group situation allows a greater degree of "acting out" of neurotic tendencies. In analysis, the temptation to "act out" neurotic tendencies is ordinarily considered a menace. The patient escapes awareness of anxiety through the discharge of tensions that result from an "acting out" of neurotic drives. The aim in analysis, therefore, is to suppress the "acting out" and to deal with the patient's subjective awareness of anxiety. The opportunity to actually live out neurotic tendencies in the group situation, if carefully controlled, proves to some extent to be an advantage.

While it is true that this "acting out" may conceal latent anxiety, it is nevertheless also true that the "living out" of neurotic tendencies in the context of the multiple interpersonal patterns of the group, provides an opportunity for a detailed analysis of character traits as, for example, a chronic tendency to failure, a drive for perfection, or a tendency for emotional isolation. The inappropriateness and inefficiency of such maladaptive patterns can be strikingly demonstrated in a group. Sometimes when a patient feels the full impact of the irrationality of his behavior within the actual social situation of the group, intense anxiety is stimulated which, in turn, can be therapeutically exploited. Another point worthy of emphasis is that the "acting out" level of experience provides for a significant emotional release on a predominantly motor level, which is advantageous. In general, the therapist must play a more active role in the group than in the psychoanalytic situation.

Group Psychotherapy, operating on an interpersonal level different from that in psychoanalysis, yet gains much from applying psychoanalytic insight to the dynamics of group living. On the whole, Group Therapy is a more real experience than is individual therapy. It is less bound to the irrationalities of the unconscious and is weighted on the side of social reality. Its greatest effectiveness seems to be in the area of re-integration of ego-adaptive patterns with resulting improvement of social functioning.

Chapter Eight

INTERVIEW GROUP PSYCHOTHERAPY WITH ALLERGY PATIENTS

Allergists have found that emotional disturbances often impede or vitiate the medical treatment of their patients. The connection between allergic symptoms and psychological factors has often been noted, and psychotherapeutic treatment of allergic patients through the utilization of individual psychotherapy has been described.[1] This chapter is devoted to a report on the psychologic treatment of allergic patients through Group Therapy, either exclusively or in combination with individual therapy.

The group consisted of the therapists' private patients, and met once a week in sessions of one-and-a-half hour's duration. It was composed of both allergic and non-allergic patients. Patients were enrolled for a series of fifteen sessions and were allowed to re-enroll as they wished for subsequent series of the same number of sessions.

The patients included in the present study were all those allergic patients enrolled in Group IV; i.e. in the fourth series of sessions. They displayed various clinical manifestations of allergy which had persisted for varying lengths of time as shown in Table I. The majority had been referred because their response to medical treatment alone had been unsatisfactory.

[1] French, T. M. and Alexander, F.: *Psychogenic Factors in Bronchial Asthma.* Psychosomatic Medicine Monograph number 2, 1941; Rogerson, C.H., et al: A Psychological Approach to the Problem of Asthma and the Asthma, Eczema, Prurigo Syndrome. *Guy's Hosp. Rep.* 1935; Saul, L. and Bernstein, C: The Emotional Settings of Some Attacks of Urticaria, *Psychosom. Med.,* October, 1941.

Table I

Diagnoses and Duration of Allergic Symptoms

Case No.	Age	Diagnosis	Duration
F/1	28	Perennial asthma Perennial hay fever Migraine	16 years
F/2	24	Perennial asthma Perennial hay fever Neurodermatitis	Since infancy
M/4	25	Perennial hay fever Eczema	Since infancy
M/5	40	Perennial asthma Perennial hay fever	35 years
M/6	38	Perennial hay fever	7 years
M/7	32	Perennial asthma	Since infancy
F/8	30	Perennial hay fever	25 years
F/9	38	Perennial asthma Perennial hay fever	Since childhood
M/10	32	Perennial asthma Perennial hay fever	10 years
M/11	27	Perennial asthma	Since childhood

There were 10 allergic patients; 6 men and 4 women. The group in which they were enrolled numbered 20 members; 10 men and 10 women. The ages of the total group ranged from 24 to 40 years with a mean of 33.5. In the allergics the age range was from 24 to 38 years, with a mean of 31.4, while in the non-allergics the range was from 27 to 40 years, with a mean of 35.6. The following Table shows other elements in the composition of the group.

Table II

Showing Composition of Group IV

	Allergic	Non-Allergic	Total
Married[2]	6	7	13
Single	1	1	2
Divorced	3	2	5
Protestants	4	5	9
Catholics	1	1	2
Jewish	5	4	9

Occupations included a salesperson, a laboratory technician, a labor organizer, an engineer, several secretaries, students, teachers and housewives.

Fourteen of the 20 members of the group, 8 allergics, 6 non-allergics, had attended previous courses. Six, 2 allergics, 4 non-allergics, were new patients. Up to the date of reporting the new patients had attended 9 sessions. The remaining allergic members had previously attended from 15 to 45 sessions having been in Group Therapy from 3 months to 1 year. Seven of the allergics had individual psychotherapy once or twice a week for all or part of the time that they were in the group.

Since the term Group Therapy has had such varied implications, a brief description will help to define the nature of the present group and its functioning.

As cited in another paper,[3] orientation in the present instance was to a type of group discussion characterized above all by permissiveness. Sessions were held in a private home. In the beginning the therapist had assumed major responsibility for establishing a warm, friendly and informal atmosphere which then

[2] Among these were three married couples, M/6 and F/15, M/19 and F/8, M/20 and F/9. It has been a policy in admitting married couples to require that one attend the group alone before admission of the other, and that the second be admitted only on the expressed desire of the first.

[3] Baruch, Dorothy W.: Description of a Project in Group Therapy, *J. Consult. Psychol.* Sept.–Oct., 1945.

spontaneously perpetuated itself. Members called each other and the therapist and allergist, who was present at all sessions, by their first names. They sat informally on chairs and on the floor in a rough circle of which both the allergist and therapist were a part. Although the therapist and allergist left soon after the therapy sessions were over, some of the group members remained. They either discussed among themselves what had transpired at the group session, or they spent the time in a purely social way. Gradually close friendships developed which continued outside the sessions.

After group rapport had been established, a professional visitor was occasionally permitted to attend. His identity was given and the fact acknowledged that his presence might inhibit free discussion. This acknowledgment in itself appeared to set the group at ease.

Stenographic records were made of all sessions. Here again, the presence of the stenographer and the purpose of making a record were frankly discussed. Several points were brought forth: first, that the records would serve the group members themselves, since they would be available to them at any time to catch up on any meetings missed and to evaluate their own progress; second, that accurate records would also serve for purposes of research, giving the group an opportunity to help others. Members of the group were asked to comment on and correct reports based on these records before they were presented or published. Invariably this met with active and cooperative response.

Discussion was the main method utilized,[4] with occasional psychodrama, drawing or writing interspersed. The psychotherapist served as leader, the allergist functioning at times as co-leader and at other times as a group member.

The therapist had brought out with Group I at the beginning of the first series of sessions that the major function of group members was to talk about the feelings that troubled them. However, it was also indicated that talking was not essential

---

[4] For a more detailed description of the sort of discussion techniques used in the group see Baruch, Dorothy W.: Description of a Project in Group Therapy. *ibid.*

unless one felt like it. The therapist had stressed that all conversations would have to be kept in strictest confidence, and had defined some of the mechanics for carrying on discussions, such as avoidance of asides, the importance of raising one's hand before speaking, and the like. In subsequent groups, the old members clarified these points to new members. The therapist's function throughout consisted mainly in keeping discussion focused on emotional content, in clarifying what the group expressed, and in helping understand collective meanings and applicability.

She helped members to put into words feelings that expressed themselves in psychomotor tensions, evasiveness, breaks in the discussion and similar manifestations. She attempted to keep discussion dispersed in order to prevent the more aggressive members from overshadowing the less aggressive ones, and to avoid any one person's exposing himself so fast as either to engender too intense feelings of guilt within himself or rejection by other members. When possible, she helped to bring intragroup hostilities and tensions into the open so that these might be worked through. Throughout, the therapist maintained, and helped others maintain, a non-advisory role, keeping the emphasis on release and acceptance.

The following excerpt translates some of these generalizations into the group members' own terms. It comes from the fourth session after admission of new members into Group IV.

F/22 [5] (New member) [6]	I want to know, when we tell about the things that have troubled us, doesn't anyone ever say there's a better way of handling them?
M/4 (Old member) [6]	Why don't you try cornering Dorothy (Therapist) to give you advice (Laughing)?
Therapist	(Laughing): Would she give it? F/22 is

[5] F/22 signifies female case 22; M/4 male case 4, etc. See table I.

[6] Old member designates a member who has attended previous series of group therapy sessions; new member designates one whose initial entry was into the series under discussion, i. e. Group IV.

bothered about having no suggestions or advice.

F/8 (Old member)	You have to go to Mr. Anthony for that.
Therapist	How about some of you others? Haven't you had the same feelings as F/22?
F/12 (Old member)	I think we all felt bewildered about it at first. But after I'd spilled enough, the answers suddenly began to dawn on me.
Therapist	You feel you work things out when you express enough of your unwanted feelings. What have some of the rest of you found?
M/7 (New member)	Actually you take things out and look at them and then have the feeling, what made me hide them before?
M/11 (New member)	The only reason I would like to have some solutions offered is that maybe I haven't thought of everything.
Therapist	You feel you still have a desire for advice.
M/11 (New member)	I tend to intellectualize too much and that is why I want an intellectual answer.
Therapist	(Nodding) What do some of you feel has happened after you've gotten things out?
F/13 (Old member)	It brings quite a sense of relief.
F/16 (Old member)	But it's different from doing it by yourself. If I spill to myself I just flounder around and never find a solution. You have kept saying to bring these things out and I would gradually be able to solve them because my approach would be different. If any of you had given me advice I wouldn't have followed it anyway. Advice wouldn't have helped but the truth that comes from within your-

self helps you take a different approach.
I needed to repeat and repeat things,
but then when a problem was solved,
I've been helped to get on to something
new.

F/2 (Old member)   I've liked to find out things for myself.
When I did, it made me feel good.

The above shows that new members were groping for advice,
whereas old members had developed a feeling for the therapeutic
value of release. In the last statement quoted, F/2 summarized
the fact that the group had given an opportunity for independent
solution of problems which her own family, incidentally, had
not provided. From the comments of F/16 it is evident that the
group simultaneously furnished support. It is also apparent that
the therapist called for group expression on the various individual
opinions, thus keeping meanings collective and discussion dispersed.

Another excerpt from the same meeting illustrates how members bring forth their reactions to each other and release tensions
so that they may be worked through and not interfere permanently with intra-group rapport.

F/12 (Old member)   I still feel very strange with this new
group. Everybody has looked so much
stranger than they should have.

F/13 (Old member)   I always have that feeling when a new
group begins. It is still difficult for me to
adjust myself to new faces.

F/16 (Old member)   I have a feeling of hostility. It's like
meeting anything new, a feeling of fear.

F/8 (Old Member)   We regard Dorothy and Hy as parents,
and when new members come in it's
like having a new baby come along.

The new members then voiced some of their feelings of strange-
ness and of having been excluded. In the interchange a better
sense of group integration appeared to evolve.

It is interesting to note in F/8's comment that the therapist and allergist were accepted in mother and father roles. This attitude was common in the group.

It must be remembered that this was the fourth series of group therapy sessions which included a number of patients who belonged to groups before. After they resolved their initial resistance to the new members and by virtue of their ability to communicate freely, they helped release the newcomers and accelerate their progress.

As reported in earlier papers, it became apparent also here that the allergic individual uses his allergy for one or the other or for all of three major purposes.[7] Briefly these are: (1) To gain response, affection, attention and sympathy of which he has been, or feels he has been, deprived, usually through maternal rejection.[8] (2) To express hostility and aggression for having been denied or frustrated in obtaining essential physical or emotional satisfactions. (3) To conceal emotions that have made him feel guilty, anxious or ashamed.

In the framework of the type of group described, he gains the responses he unconsciously craves. He has here also the opportunity to release hostility and aggression, to eliminate the need for canalizing them into his symptoms, and to lessen guilt and anxiety which had been similarly assuaged.

The foregoing brief quotations from the discussions show how the supporting nature of the group is capable of contributing the first need; namely, acceptance and response. The material to follow aims at showing that within the emotional climate created in the group, the allergic moves through fairly well-defined emotional phases and that these are synchronized with characteristic somatic manifestations.

In the first phase in Group Therapy the allergic individual is inhibited. He continues to repress and block the expression of

[7] Miller, Hyman and Baruch, Dorothy W.: Group and Individual Psychotherapy as an Adjunct in the Diagnosis and Treatment of Allergy, Presented before the American Academy of Allergy, New York, December, 1946.

[8] Baruch, Dorothy W., and Miller, Hyman: Group and Individual Psychotherapy as an Adjunct in the Treatment of Allergy, J. Consult. Psychol., Sept.–Oct., 1946.

negative feelings. This phase is accompanied by frequent somatic attacks. In the second phase he releases negative feelings but vacillates between release and repression. Guilt and anxiety appear at this stage, but while release is in ascendance, somatic symptoms diminish. When guilt and anxiety assume the ascendance, the symptoms are aggravated. Gradually expression of hostility is accompanied by a decreasing intensity of guilt and anxiety which in turn diminish the frequency and severity of the attacks. This third or last phase may be accompanied by insight into the patients' problems, though it is the impression of the present writers that the actual flow or release of emotions is the more essential factor. This process was brought out by one of the members of the group, M/5, when he said during one of the group discussions: "I can't work up a good honest hate. I start, then I get to feeling guilty over it and take it out on myself and get moody and I shut in my feelings or block them and get asthma instead."

The following accounts further illustrate these dynamics in relation to the group therapy experienced by several allergic patients.

M/4 was 25 years old, a veteran of World War II, having served in combat zones in the South Pacific. He had received a medical discharge because of allergy approximately one year prior to referral to the allergist. His complaint was perennial hay fever of ten years' duration and a skin eruption since infancy which he related to diet and "nervousness." A physical examination showed a typical allergic eczema limited to the right forearm and hand, and a characteristic allergic nasal mucosa. Skin tests were markedly positive to many types of pollen and food. Immunization with pollen antigens was carried on regularly and persistently from January 1945 to the date of the present report. At the end of the nine months of treatment, the hay fever symptoms showed a fair degree of improvement, but despite continuation of medical treatment marked exacerbations occurred frequently. The eczema showed little if any improvement despite the removal of the reacting foods from the diet. It was this lack of improvement together with the patient's difficulty in making an adjustment to civilian life, although a year had passed since his discharge from the army, that led to referral to Group Therapy.

On entry into the group he was extremely shut in and reticent. He said that nothing was wrong in his life except "nervousness," which, he claimed, was due to the army and his current divorce. He sat through three group sessions without participating. His face was devoid of all expression. At the end of the third session, during which various group members had talked about disturbing family relationships in their past, he commented: "Why talk about the past, I never think about the past, why keep dwelling on it?" In the fourth session he said: "I just don't seem to fit in here, I guess I'm different. I've never had any trouble like the rest." And he reiterated: "I don't see how the past has anything to do with how I feel now. I don't see how it can affect you when you're grown up and anyway, I never had anything that bothered me in my childhood. My folks were always good to me, they spoiled me, they weren't strict or anything. It's the army that got me, it made me ready to argue with everybody about everything."

He maintained this attitude throughout the first course of Group Therapy sessions and during this period had continuous attacks of hay fever. Toward the end of the course however, in spite of his protests that nothing bothered him, he asked for individual therapy. This he received first on a once-a-week basis and later, at his own request, it was increased to twice a week concomitantly with the group sessions. In the second session of the second course—actually his thirteenth group session and following his third individual session—he admitted for the first time that all had not been well in his relationship with his parents.

The other members of the group had been talking about how their parents had hurt them as children. He said:

"I'll never forget the time I had an infected hand. It was pretty bad. My mother treated it. One night we went to dinner at a restaurant. Even in the restaurant she had to change the bandage, so she dragged me into the ladies room. I was six or seven, and I was so embarrassed. At other times my mother used to worry about my health. If there was a hard downpour, she'd send someone over to school with my raincoat and rubbers. It aggravated me."

Later on in the same session after other members of the group had been talking about how they had gotten even with their parents he said:

> "I got even one day. I came home for lunch and it was a vegetable plate and I wouldn't eat it. Mother said I could go back to school without any lunch and I did, only first I went over to a friend's house and said my mother wasn't home and I got some lunch there. There was a certain satisfaction. I got even and I didn't eat the vegetable plate, but I had some lunch anyway."

Severe hay fever was reported to the allergist on the following day, despite the fact that the time of year was February and not the pollen season. The attacks probably represented a guilt reaction since in the next session M/4 admitted to feeling badly after having spoken as he had.

In the same session the other group members talked about feeling of dirtiness in connection with elimination. To quote:

F/3	As a little girl I used to wet the bed. I used to hate to go to bed, fearing maybe I'd have an accident.
Therapist	Those were horrible feelings.
F/3	What happens when even big people dream they're going to the lavatory and have an accident in bed?
Therapist	That's miserable, too.
F/13	My mother told me I was housebroken at a year.
F/17	I remember when I was about two years old a girl friend took down her pants in back of the garage and did her business. I thought it was awful.
M/5	When I was about ten some of the boys would pull down their pants and the other boys would do acts with them. I think there's something in that that makes me shy with other men. I never connected it until this minute: a kind of fear of other men because of that.

At this point M/4 volunteered:

"I remember when I was a kid, one day my dad came in and I wanted him to draw me a picture and he drew me one of me sitting on the toilet and after that I never cared to have anyone draw pictures any more."

In his next individual session he admitted having felt guilty over talking about his father in a derogatory way. Again he had severe hay fever.

The oscillation between releasing resentment and feeling guilty continued with concomitant hay fever attacks until the fifteenth group session, at which time the patient had also had twenty individual sessions. In the group session death wishes against parents were expressed by several members of the group. It is interesting to note that M/4 said nothing. He was silent all through. Three days later however, in his individual session he said:

"Since hearing things in the group like in the last meeting I realize for the first time in my life that my folks did things for me only because they had to. They really didn't want to. They really didn't want me."

Through identification with other group members and through his realization that they still were decent people, although they had openly shown hostility, he began to feel that he too could be decent in spite of the hostility he had revealed. This gave him courage to face the fact of having been rejected, which further justified the resentment he had felt. The resulting relief was evident in his whole attitude and his hay fever cleared and remained clear for over a month, well beyond the onset of the pollen hay fever season in June. In June of the preceding year he had had very severe symptoms despite medical treatment.

The next exacerbation came when he failed a state board examination. At this time he felt not only disgust with life but, above all, disgust with himself. He blocked the outflow of hostility to his parents and turned it inward against himself. These dynamics became apparent in the group therapy session three days after the severe attack. The group had been talking about how the different members had worked out their hostile feelings against their parents. Some members of the group including M/4 seemed to be groping for, but unable to find a formulation of their own reactions. The therapist suggested that acting out some scenes from their childhood might bring these into sharper focus. M/4 volunteered and said he would like to re-enact a scene with his mother; "Nobody else."

M/4	(Explaining to the group): It's morning and it's snowing and I want to go out and play. I'm about eight or nine. Everybody else is out playing and I want to go out, too. (He turns to the group member whom he has chosen to take the part of his mother, and whom he has told what he wanted done.) It's snowing out and everybody else is out. I want to go out and play.
F/8	You had a cold last week. You can't go out.
M/4	I'm over the cold.
F/8	Don't argue with me. I said no. I'm your mother and I said you can't go out. I don't want to hear any more about it.
M/4	But, mother, the other kids are out playing.
F/8	You're my child and I said you can't go out and you can't. That's the end of it.
M/4	(Turning to the group) That would be it. Then I'd begin wishing I was dead. I'd go to bed and I'd wish it.
Therapist	Suppose you lie down and show how you felt.
M/4	(Following the group's suggestions, puts two chairs together as a bed.) If I only had enough nerve! There's a window over there I'd jump out of. Since I haven't enough nerve, all I can do is hate myself. I should run away. But I can't. I hate myself. I wish I were dead.

Other members of the group acted out scenes from their lives, as well, showing how they had worked out their hostilities. After the release gained in this session, M/4 was clear of his hay fever for three months. Then he again failed an examination and turned his hostility back on himself. "I'm stupid," he said, "really stupid. I don't do anything right. I can't pass. I'm not worthy of it." He hesitated and said: "And I can't get back any more to hating my parents, it's been gone. I can't get back."

This blocking lasted only a short time, however. He began once more to release hostility to his parents, particularly to his mother. Then his hay fever cleared and remained so. It had been noticeable all along that hay fever exacerbations occurred whenever M/4's release of hostility to his parents was blocked and when guilt appeared to be in ascendance.

Toward the end of this period M/4 began, along with the other members of the group, to bring forth sex problems. At this time, although the hay fever had cleared, there was a marked skin eruption. Again the same dynamics became apparent. At first he insisted that sex did not bother him, that he did not feel guilty over any expression of sex. During this period his skin became very bad. Then as he brought out his feelings of anxiety and guilt and talked about his sex practices and fantasies and as he wrote and drew, and in individual sessions dramatized them with clay figures, his skin eruption cleared and did not return.

When a patient was in both group and individual therapy, material brought out in the group often carried over into individual sessions and appeared to stimulate therapeutic progress. This was well brought out in the case of F/9.

F/9 was a thirty-eight year old married woman who had had perennial asthma since an attack of acute bronchitis at the age of five years and perennial hay fever since the age of twelve. Attacks of both had occurred daily prior to entry into the group. Physical examination showed the nasal and bronchial manifestations characteristic of allergy. Skin tests taken for the first time shortly after entry into Group Therapy showed skin sensitivity to many pollens, environmental substances and foods. Medical treatment had been entirely symptomatic and palliative. No immunization had ever been attempted nor was it instituted at this time.

She was an apparently open and warm person, able to verbalize, who complained of anxieties and depressions which she said did not show externally. She had been married for eleven years and had had continuous difficulty in adjusting both on a sexual and emotional basis. She had had some previous psychotherapy and asked that both she and her husband be admitted to the present group.

Material from both individual and group sessions showed that since childhood there had been great conflict between F/9's desire for closeness and a fear of intimacy. In her sixth group session she told about how as a child, she had reached out for her mother's breast and had been violently repulsed. "It was just as though I had hurt her. I suddenly got very embarrassed about it. After that I never felt as close."

In her tenth group session the members focused on sex. That night, as reported in her individual treatment session of the following day, she had a dream about an octopus which threatened to attack and envelop her. Her associations to this brought her to an awareness of her fear of closeness and of its being somehow related to sex.

She went home and, as she later reported, tried to get at sex memories and fantasies, but found that she was blocked. Two nights later she had a dream in which a hand put soap chips into a wallet. She had a feeling that there had been sex dreams before this but that this dream blotted them out. In associating to this dream she brought out that the soap chips reminded her of "semen and the discharge you give off to make sex relations better." The wallet was "something in which you keep valuable things shut up." She woke up during the dream and had a severe attack of asthma. Severe attacks continued during the following week. During this period she also had many quarrels with her husband. In the following group session there was much talk about sex and repeated references to it as a means of gaining closeness and emotional response. Her husband, M/20, related among other things, that in his first adolescent sex episode he had sought the closeness and warm response which his parents had never given him.

The next day in her individual session, F/9 analyzed the wallet dream to mean her shutting in of sex impulses. She reported that during the group session she had felt an overwhelming sexual desire "for the first time in ages." She recounted that when she got home she had felt more for her husband than ever before.

"He's so uncommunicative and isolated most of the time that I lose sight of his wanting affection. Then last night I was touched hearing that he had had such a feeling of failure in that love affair. I connected it with my octopus dream. Our difficulties had been *me* partly. I'd kept away because I was afraid if I let him come too close he'd hurt me. After that I went out to him more warmly and he just ate it up. I got very warm and sympathetic. I played around and petted him and he just melted. Before that I'd been afraid of being hurt and I'd been hostile in order to keep him away."

All this, she said, had come to her after the group session. That night, for the first time in years, she had gone to bed without medication and had no attack of asthma. She laughed when she told of this, remarking: "And I should have had asthma because it was foggy and fog always brings it on."

M/11 was a twenty-seven year old man, recently married, shortly after discharge from the merchant marine. The persistent, severe, perennial asthma from which he had suffered since infancy, had cleared during his service except for severe attacks on returning home for a visit. Physical examination showed the characteristic changes in the nasal mucosa and the typical findings in the chest which usually accompany allergic asthma. Skin tests were positive to pollen, foods and other environmental substances. No specific immunizations had ever been attempted, treatment having been limited to symptoms and to palliatives. He was referred to Group Therapy.

He was outgoing, verbalized easily, was eager to talk in the group and to get at his feelings. In his first session he joined in the

discussion of hostility to parents; afterwards, however, he felt
guilty as shown by his remarks in the following session. For example, he said of parents: "It's not a conscious thing they do to
us; their intentions are good."

He vacillated back and forth between releasing feeling and
blocking it. During this period he had frequent attacks of asthma.
In the sixth session he described what had been happening. He
said:

> "I'm beginning to realize how I've been intellectualizing
> and not really letting my emotions go. I keep catching my-
> self and shutting myself off. I feel something and instead of
> letting the feeling go on to its conclusion, it is turned away
> by some intellectual concept."

He then listened as various group members expressed ambivalence toward their mothers.

F/9   I hated my mother. But then I would make excuses
for her. I felt sorry when she died, but I didn't
really miss her at all, only now is the first time I've
been able to say this to anyone.

F/13   I had realized there were some things about my
mother that I didn't like, but for the first time last
Sunday I had the feeling that I wasn't trying to
justify her. Before that, even though I would talk
about the things I didn't like about my mother, I
kept coming back to the thought that she was doing
her best and I shouldn't criticize her. But this time
I didn't hate myself for thinking her inadequate
and weak.

F/12   I still find it difficult to accept my mother as she is.
I always try to turn it away and make excuses for
her.

M/6   I felt very strongly against my mother but I always
excused her on the ground that that was the way
she had been brought up.

F/17   How can they be both so good and so bad?

Therapist   Suppose you all close your eyes and try to get back
to when you were children and how you felt toward
your mothers. As you've said, you had both a good

mother and a bad mother. See if you can make either a drawing or a word picture of both.

M/11 wrote the following:

My good mother was hearty and generous. She threw her whole being and ability into the feelings which she understood along with me. She devoted much thought and effort to giving me the chance to do what I liked to do, if she, too, felt it was good. My good mother entered into all my physical activities with gusto. My good mother was kind and lots of fun, and I loved her very much. My good mother never thought, only felt.

My bad mother tore the heart out of me by not understanding my more secret feeling and thoughts. My bad mother would trod roughshod over my opinions and beliefs that would not agree with hers. My bad mother engendered my active hatred by her intolerance of feelings contrary or strange to hers. She refused to recognize (and still does) the possibility of other values than hers. This caused her to be tactless and undiplomatic so that she would embarrass me before others. What I held most against her was that she treated my closest feelings with contempt and disdain. Everything subtle was beyond her. I yearned to be understood and she refused to try, and I hated my bad mother. This was her blank side.

After reading this, M/11 said: "I never realized before that I had two mothers." He went on talking about the mother he had "hated," ending: "She would embarrass me by bringing out things to other people that I didn't want them to know about and I hated her for that." Then he quickly added: "But I really do love and admire her, for she has lots of gusto."

The group then got into talk of having felt rejected.

F/12   Is it possible to vaguely remember things when you were two or so? Now suddenly my mother has me up in her arms—up high—and I have a feeling that I'm going to fall—that she is going to throw me down. She talks about how I fell out of my crib when I was two. But I have a feeling now that she

	dropped me. I feel her hatred. Could it have really been so?
Therapist	(Nodding) Even if she did not actually drop you, you could have felt she wanted to.
F/12	She wanted to bash me on the ground.
M/5	(Nodded)
Therapist	M/5 looks as if he understood this feeling.

The discussion continued along the same vein. M/11 grew silent and was obviously upset.

During the week following this session anxiety apparently overwhelmed him. He was blocked even in his work.

At the next session he started almost immediately wheezing and laboring for breath. These symptoms were relieved by an injection of epinephrine. At the end of this session, after listening to others speak freely, he said he felt better emotionally as well as physically. In the following session he expressed hostility freely and since then has had no asthma.

Although the course of treatment had not ended, four patients in this group showed complete clearing of physical symptoms. Three were markedly improved. Two were somewhat improved; one showed no change.

Paralleling the degree of improvement in terms of physical symptoms the patients appeared more at ease, less tense and more outgoing. They reported having less difficulties in personal relationships and adjustments; they felt more self-confidence and, with one exception, cited specific instances of more adequate functioning.

The following are illustrative of remarks concerning changes they felt within themselves. F/2, a timid unmarried girl of twenty-four, suffering from neurodermatitis had been unable to free herself from her parents. Before group treatment, she had been extremely immature and dependent and had lost one job after another. She had no individual therapy. After fifteen group sessions her skin had completely cleared. She reported: "I can handle my parents much better and feel freer with them. They don't bother me nearly as much. . . . I don't feel so shy. I can express myself better and I'm being more successful. I can put myself across better. I've managed to stick to my job and have even gotten higher pay."

F/1, a married woman of twenty-eight years, had entered the group, having had asthma, hay fever and migraine for sixteen years. She was withdrawn, shy and apprehensive. She sat and listened attentively, but rarely spoke. Her physical symptoms nonetheless improved markedly. That the group meant a great deal to her was evidenced by the fact that she invariably stayed after the therapy sessions. "For the first time in my life," she said, "I'm not too afraid to express my true thoughts at home to my family. Before long I may be able to express myself anywhere." At another time she remarked: "I understand myself better since I've been in the group; other people, too." At still another time she confided to the therapist: "I feel much less horrid."

Group Therapy parallel with medical therapy and at times with individual psychotherapy appeared to have helped most of the patients with their allergic as well as with their personality problems.

The group appeared to provide certain values for the patients, aside from greater economy. It furnished supportive relationships and contributed a sense of belonging. Through the maintenance of intra-group acceptance it gave concrete evidence that resentments and other tabooed feelings could be expressed not only to a therapist but to other people without bringing about the rejection and isolation ordinarily feared. Hearing others talk about emotions which in our culture usually produce guilt, helped the patients feel more at ease and they were able to explore and release emotions related to their allergic attacks.

Chapter Nine

INTERVIEW GROUP PSYCHOTHERAPY FOR
SPEECH DISORDERS

It is conservatively estimated that there are in the United States over ten million people who have speech and voice disorders of varying degrees of severity. In the vast majority of cases these disorders are either on a psychoneurotic basis or are coupled with superinduced psychoneurotic attitudes and reactions. Therefore, any effective treatment for these conditions must include psychotherapy.

In a problem of such magnitude, it is obviously impossible to rely solely on individual psychotherapy. To meet the demands on the limited therapeutic resources available today, it has been necessary to introduce the group approach. However, experience has shown that there is in the group medium itself a factor that wields a potent therapeutic influence on the patient, so that, quite apart from the matter of expediency, Group Therapy has become the treatment of choice for many speech and voice conditions. Its efficacy is most strikingly apparent in the treatment of stuttering.

Stuttering is a disorder characterized by repetitions of syllables or words, blockages, or other spasmodic interruptions in the rhythm of speech, and often accompanied by adventitious movements, such as tics or twitches, especially of the face. There are various types of stuttering: clonic, tonic, clonico-tonic, and tonico-clonic. In its predominantly tonic forms, stuttering is sometimes termed stammering.

There are many conflicting theories regarding the etiology of stuttering, their fundamental theses depending largely upon the

176

orientation in medicine, psychology or education of their respective proponents. This paper presents the theory[1] that stuttering speech is a somatic manifestation of an underlying personality disorder based on a psychobiologic variation involving the organism as a whole.[2] This variation does not in itself cause stuttering; the speech disorder appears to be precipitated by emotional shock, which may be traceable to an accident, a fright, some radical environmental change, such as the advent of a younger child into the family, or the accumulated impacts of a neurotic home environment. The primary fault appears to lie in the emotional stream, and a question naturally arises as to why the speech apparatus rather than some other system of the body is affected by the shock. An entirely plausible explanation is suggested by the significant work being carried on in the field of constitutional medicine. It has been shown[3] that there is often an imbalance in the various organ systems of the body and that under certain conditions, such as family discord and emotional shock, the weakest system breaks down. It is possible that the speech system is, as Leland E. Hinsie [4] has suggested, a *locus minoris resistentiae*.

Regardless of the etiology of stuttering, however, the fact remains that the confirmed stutterer presents a picture of an insecure, chronically anxious, highly excitable, narcissistic individual, emotionally immature as regards all inter-personal adjustments and morbidly fearful of speech situations. It is this warped personality as it presents itself at the time of treatment, rather than the formulation of involved theories regarding its etiology, in which the therapist is primarily interested and which he attempts to influence through group therapy.

Slavson[5] distinguishes two general types of Group Therapy:

[1] This theory is based on observation and study of some twenty-five thousand stutterers treated at the National Hospital for Speech Disorders in the course of the past thirty years.

[2] Greene, J. S.: Functional Speech and Voice Disorders. *J. Nerv. Ment. Dis.*, March, 1942.

[3] Pende, Nicola: *Constitutional Inadequacies*. Philadelphia, Lea & Febiger, 1928.

[4] Personal communication to the author.

[5] Slavson, S. R., cited by Ackerman, Nathan W.: Dynamic Patterns in Group Psychotherapy. *Psychiatry*, November, 1944.

therapy *in* the group, in which the therapist points his techniques specifically toward the needs of particular individuals in the group, with group interaction playing a secondary role; and therapy *through* the group, which relies for its therapeutic efficacy on the "modifying effect of interacting relationship patterns within the group, with the therapist playing for the most part a recessive role." In the treatment of stuttering, both techniques are profitably employed. The therapist often finds it advisable to initiate discussions and to take advantage of situations arising in the group to give a certain amount of interpretation.[6] Although such interpretation is usually given to the individual patient within the group, it is often applicable to the other members as well and serves to stimulate a general discussion. The therapist takes a leading role in directing the course of the discussion, but the interacting influence of the various members of the group on one another constitutes a most important therapeutic factor.

The aim of the group approach in the treatment of stuttering is threefold: (1) to break down the stutterer's old, unsound emotional reactions, habit patterns and attitudes, and to help him build up healthy, constructive new ones; (2) to overcome the patient's specific fears and anxieties, especially regarding speech

---

[6] No attempt at "deep analysis" is made. The type of interpretation given at the National Hospital for Speech Disorders is suggested by the following incident: The therapist, having been called out of the group, re-entered the room and addressed a question to a boy of nineteen who had been talking loudly and fluently to his neighbor. The patient immediately began to stutter. When queried as to why he was unable to talk to the therapist although he had been speaking without difficulty a moment before, the patient shook his head to indicate that he could offer no explanation. Acquainted with the boy's family history and aware of the early influence of a domineering father, the therapist suggested that perhaps he, by virtue of his position in the group, had become for the patient a father surrogate and that the boy, on suddenly being confronted with him, had been assailed by feelings of guilt and by fear of punishment for his "misbehavior." The therapist then explained how a fear of authority, founded on early fear of the parent, affected the individual's reactions to the world at large. At this point, a provocative question from another patient led the therapist to a discussion of the way in which, through the superego, old parental codes continue in later life to exert their influence on the individual.

situations; (3) to foster a better social adjustment and to develop a more mature, more adequate, and better integrated personality as a whole.

To accomplish these ends several groups are used. The new patient is placed in what might be termed a "low pressure" group in which the seemingly hostile aspects of the outside world, which constitute such mental hazards for the stutterer, have been for the most part removed. The atmosphere is tolerant and accepting; the patient is made to feel that whatever his attitude, reactions or shortcomings, he is accepted without reservation. As he adjusts to the group milieu, he progresses to more advanced groups, the therapist being careful throughout treatment not to force him beyond his carrying power. As Schilder[7] stated some years ago: "We should not demand too much. Such demands are useless and increase the sense of failure in the patient." To avoid this pitfall and other traumatizing impacts, therapy must be so devised as to submit the stutterer to a gradual increase of environmental pressure in proportion to his growing ability to withstand it.

A certain amount of speech re-education, carried out in the group medium, is introduced to give the patient an opportunity to "act against his symptom" and to prove to him that in a state of emotional equilibrium he can verbalize normally. Thus, by repeatedly and successfully facing the situation toward which he has had most anxiety, he gradually breaks down his fear response to it. However, informal discussion is the pivotal activity within the group; and in this connection those who treat stutterers have one extremely important advantage over many other workers in the field of group therapy—the factor of homogeneity. Stutterers all suffer from what might be termed a social neurosis. Their anxiety and speech symptom comes to the fore in the social setting and, as has already been pointed out, they all present essentially similar problems and personality deviations. Since this is so, most of the individual patient's problems can be discussed openly; and through this "open-door psychotherapy," thoughts,

[7] Schilder, Paul: *Psychotherapy*, New York, W. W. Norton and Co., 1938.

feelings and conflicts that previously gave rise to anxiety and feelings of shame and self depreciation, lose much of their damaging and distorting effects upon the patient's psyche.

Not all problems, of course, lend themselves to this open discussion technique, and Group Therapy is necessarily supplemented by individual interviews, the amount of individual work depending upon the specific needs of the patient. In both, group and individual treatment, an effort is made to have the patient realize his limitations and to help him effect an harmonious compromise between those limitations and the demands of the environment.

Psychotherapy is supplemented by other supportive group measures such as clubs, choral and dramatic groups, dancing, games, and various other social activities. Under the influence of this multiple treatment, the stutterer in time develops a more secure, more stable, more confident personality, capable of withstanding the stresses of everyday living without becoming disorganized, capable, in other words, of adjusting on a more nearly normal level to the demands of reality.

The history of Daniel Wright[8] illustrates the efficacy of Group Therapy in a case in which individual psychotherapy had been tried with limited success:

Daniel, a boy of sixteen and the son of a psychiatrist, had been receiving individual psychiatric assistance for some time when he was referred for Group Therapy. On examination, he showed several physiologic disturbances indicative of tension and anxiety: cold, moist palms; a rapid, labile pulse; and hyperactive deep reflexes. Speech production was characterized by marked tonic spasms of the articulatory mechanism, which caused a severe stutter, and by unpleasant grimaces.

Under Group Therapy, the patient made excellent progress and within a few weeks was playing a leading role in one of the informal sketches arranged by the dramatic group. At the end

[8] This and subsequent cases cited are taken from the records of the National Hospital for Speech Disorders.

of three months, he returned to school and his father reported favorably on the improvement in the boy's speech and the changes in his personality. The boy himself reported a marked diminution of his anxiety. The following summer, the patient again spent a few weeks under group treatment, after which he felt that he had attained a degree of stability which would permit him to terminate his contact with the clinic. He is now taking a pre-medical course in college and is making a good adjustment.

Group psychotherapy has an important role in the treatment of hysterical aphonia.

Hysterical aphonia may be defined as loss of voice due to psychic factors. The onset of the disorder is usually sudden, the patient finding it impossible to speak above a whisper or (in some cases) being unable to phonate at all. The condition develops much more often in women than in men and most typically represents a psychic escape from some environmental situation which is distasteful to the individual or which threatens his security or happiness, as in the case of Zena Lieb:

Mrs. Lieb, a married woman of forty-seven, presented herself for treatment stating that she had lost her voice several weeks before, following a cold.[9] Various therapeutic measures had been tried, but to no avail. These had included a rest cure away from home.

The patient declared that she was completely happy, but the anamnesis subsequently revealed that her aged mother and uncle lived with her and that their demands on her were sources of much irritation and tension. She had a deep sense of filial obligation and protested that she carried her burden willingly. However, it was evident that while consciously she was resigned to the circumstances, unconsciously she resented them and had resorted to the aphonia in order to escape from them. The loss of voice, suggesting some organic condition, gave her a legitimate excuse to withdraw from the unpleasant situation, at least tempo-

---

[9] A history of a "cold," an attack of "laryngitis," or "voice strain" is typical, the patient unconsciously striving to establish the organic plausibility of his symptom.

rarily, and to demand more consideration from her family because she was ostensibly "ill."

Occasionally hysterical aphonia develops as an attention getting device or as a sequel to trauma, as in the case of Roberta Lawson:

Mrs. Lawson, a married woman of thirty-six, was a mill worker of limited intelligence. Upon presenting herself for treatment she related in a barely audible whisper that her voice difficulty dated from a quarrel with her husband, three years before. The anamnesis disclosed that the patient's marital life had been most unhappy. Her husband was a philanderer and frequently abusive. Discovering that he was the father of a child by another woman, the patient had confronted him with accusations of his infidelity. A bitter quarrel ensued, during which he violently choked her.

Immediately after the choking episode, the patient found that she could not talk above a whisper and could scarcely move her jaw or lips. When she was seen in the clinic three years later there was still an almost complete absence of jaw or lip movements, a fact which initially suggested Bell's palsy. However, examination revealed no pathologic condition to account for this or for the aphonia.

This case is particularly interesting in that it illustrates a general tendency of the person who develops hysterical symptoms following some traumatic experience to demonstrate the condition as he thinks it *would have developed* if there had actually been an injury. In this case the patient unconsciously assumed that, since the jaw, lips and throat are concerned in speech production, an injury such as she imagined herself to have received would have affected the functions of them all.

With few exceptions, patients who develop hysterical aphonia possess certain characteristics in common. They seemingly find it difficult under conditions of stress to make a mature adjustment to reality. Their emotional reactions remain on an adolescent level, and there is usually evidence of emotional instability long before the onset of the aphonia. The acute symptom itself seems to be only a part of a larger "pattern response." [10] They are abnormally suggestible, egocentric, and prone to self dramatization; and, unlike the majority of other speech and voice sufferers, they are not unduly sensitive about their voice disorder.

Hysterical aphonia does not offer any special diagnostic problem for the physician. Upon superficial examination the appearance of the larynx may suggest an organic bilateral adductor paralysis,[11] but if the patient can be induced to cough, or if upon the introduction of a drop of saline solution into the larynx the cords fly together reflexly from the resultant irritation, the fact that no true paralysis exists is established. A careful anamnesis will confirm the diagnosis of hysterical aphonia.

It is usually possible to restore the voice through suggestion, but more extensive psychotherapy is essential if the patient is to be permanently benefited. The more immediate aim of psychotherapy, after the voice has been restored, is to remove the factors in the environment that have precipitated the disorder or to change the patient's attitude toward them. The ultimate aim, of course, is to develop a more mature personality. This necessitates individual psychiatric treatment, but Group Psychotherapy is a valuable adjuvant. The typical emotional and intellectual immaturity of the patient who develops hysterical aphonia at first precludes her acceptance of any completely candid explanation of the etiology of her condition; such an "expose" usually leads to resentment and resistance to further therapeutic procedures. However, when he discovers, through the medium of the group, that other patients have psychic conflicts which they have attempted to solve by various neurotic compromises similar to his own, his resistance to insight lessens and he is better able to work through his problems to a more satisfactory solution. Group Therapy has the further advantage, especially in those cases in which the aphonia has persisted over a prolonged period of dis-

---

[10] Greene, J. S.: Voice Anomalies of Hysteric Origin. *The Eye, Ear, Nose and Throat Monthly*, May, 1940.

[11] Richards, Lyman G.: *Otolaryngology in General Practice*, New York, Macmillan Co., 1939.

pelling the patient's fears that his voice may again fail. The cumulative effects of repeated successes in speaking before the group serve to allay the patient's anticipatory doubts and to reinforce his self confidence.

Psychophonasthenia is another voice condition in which the most effective therapy combines group and individual treatment.

Psychophonasthenia is a disorder, psychic in origin, characterized by a tremulous, pinched voice that breaks suddenly to a lower key or momentarily chokes off completely. It most frequently afflicts men and women in professional life or in executive positions who feel inadequate to the demands placed upon them, and whose anxiety has been physiologized in the vocal tract. The patient is tense, anxious and apprehensive; and although he is usually above average in intelligence, emotionally he is immature and unstable. Chronically assailed by feelings of insecurity and inferiority, he is asocial and retiring. Evidence will usually disclose that these characteristics were well marked before the appearance of the voice disorder itself, suggesting that psychophonasthenia is the culmination of a neurosis which has been developing over a long period.

Individual psychiatric treatment must be introduced to uncover the patient's deep rooted conflicts, but it is imperative that Group Psychotherapy have a part in the therapeutic program in order to give the patient a framework of support in which to work out his problems. Group Therapy also gives him an opportunity to develop a sense of identification with others, a feeling that is conspicuously absent in the psychophonasthenic and which is essential to the development of a sense of security.

The group techniques introduced are similar to those employed in the treatment of stuttering, the individual progressing from one group to the next as he gives evidence of greater insight into his conflicts and of increasing ability to withstand environmental pressure. In the initial stages, the patient typically offers a great deal of resistance to therapy while appearing to be genuinely cooperative. The therapist must be alert to this concealed resistance since it is a most important factor in treatment. Because of it, the treatment of psychophonasthenia usually extends over a longer period than the treatment of other psychogenic voice and speech disorders.

Group Therapy is a valuable adjuvant in the treatment of the patient with a falsetto voice.

A falsetto voice is an abnormally high, shrill voice in the adult male. Occasionally it is a symptom of glandular dysfunction, but this is less often the case than might be suspected. In the majority of instances the voice disorder appears to develop initially as a protest against assuming the adult masculine role. The patient typically gives a history of having been a shy, sensitive, somewhat neurotic child. Such a child is more than ordinarily embarrassed by the somatic changes of pubescence, and especially by the voice change which gives to the world objective evidence of his approaching maturity. In his embarrassment and his state of uncertainty, he strives to cling to the security of childhood a little longer and unconsciously inhibits the voice change. Through constant misuse of the laryngeal muscles, the levators remain in dominance, keeping the larynx high in the throat, and the childish treble becomes a permanent feature. The condition, if uncorrected, continues throughout the individual's entire life; and since a certain stigma is attached to the disorder by virtue of the fact that a high, feminine voice is characteristic of the eunuch and eunuchoid, the man with a falsetto voice is usually subjected to many traumatizing experiences which increase his sensitivity and aggravate his neurotic tendencies.

It is not a complicated therapeutic procedure to lower the larynx and thus lower the voice, but psychic factors often interfere with the permanency of the change if local treatment is not supplemented by psychotherapy. To the patient accustomed to his high, shrill voice, the new low pitch sounds unnatural; and almost invariably he is assailed by doubts as to what people may think or say about the sudden change. The patient's sensitivity on this score is occasionally so acute that he reverts to his high voice when he returns to his old environment.

Group Psychotherapy counteracts this sensitivity and its destructive effects. Furthermore, when the patient whose voice has been lowered is placed in a group of other patients who speak in the normal male range, he tends almost unconsciously to imitate the general low pitch. This aids in reinforcing the dominance of the depressor muscles of the larynx so that within a comparatively brief period it becomes well established.

Group Therapy is efficacious also in the treatment of many voice and speech conditions which are of definite organic origin. It is of particular value in the rehabilitation of the patient who has undergone laryngectomy because of cancer of the larynx.

Since teaching such a patient to develop a substitute voice by using the esophagus in place of the larynx would seem to be largely a mechanical problem, one might assume that psychic factors do not enter the picture. Actually they are extremely important. The patient who has undergone laryngectomy has usually led a full, active life until the age of forty, fifty or sixty, when he suddenly finds himself bereft of employment and normal social intercourse because of the removal of his larynx and the consequent loss of voice. The psychic trauma incident to this sudden change in economic and social status is often as serious as the physical trauma itself.[12] In a study of seventy patients who had undergone laryngectomy, 90 per cent reported that following their operations they were extremely depressed, some to the point of considering suicide. In one case, the operation precipitated a psychosis and the patient subsequently underwent shock therapy in a mental institution.

Because of the serious psychic effects of laryngectomy, postoperative treatment must embody psychological as well as re-educational procedures. Group Therapy has been found much more valuable than individual mental hygiene measures. The group approach brings the patient to a realization that his position, while unfortunate, is not unique; and contact with more advanced patients is a source of great encouragement. Group Therapy also gives the patient an opportunity to develop

[12] Greene, J. S.: Composite Postoperative Therapy for the Laryngectomized, *Medical World*, March, 1942.

his new voice through practice in a sympathetic environment. Because everyone else is in a similar plight, he does not feel self-conscious or sensitive.

In this connection, it has been noted that patients who insist on individual instruction seldom adjust as well to their changed status as do those patients who are placed in a group; and they seldom progress as rapidly in developing an esophageal voice. Probably this latter phenomenon can be explained on the basis of neuromuscular tensions. In learning to speak with an esophageal voice, the patient must aspirate air into the esophagus by a contraction of the sternohyoid, thyrohyoid, mylohyoid, and the anterior portion of the digastric muscles,[13] and then eructate—coordinating the process of eructation with the processes of phonation and articulation. This at best is a difficult procedure, and the necessary coordination is all but impossible if the patient is a prey to destructive emotions and the neuromuscular tensions they generate. The group approach, creating an optimistic atmosphere through the presence of more advanced patients, in most cases greatly reduces the emotional factor and counteracts any initial discouragement that the individual may feel.

The contrast between the cases of two patients who received voice training following laryngectomy illustrates the greater progress made by one under group stimulation.

Charles Tate, age sixty-eight, underwent laryngectomy in October, 1945. John Farrell, also sixty-eight, was operated on during the same month. The operations were performed in each case by excellent surgeons.

Both patients registered for voice training within the same week. Mr. Tate, a wealthy and socially prominent businessman, insisted on private treatment. Mr. Farrell, a dispensary patient, was placed in a free clinic group. Both patients were completely aphonic when admitted for treatment, but within three months the dispensary patient had mastered the technique of the esophageal voice and was.ready to be discharged. In contrast, the

[13] Jackson, C. J. and Jackson, C. L.: *The Larynx and Its Diseases*, Philadelphia, W. B. Saunders Co., 1937.

private patient was just beginning to produce an esophageal voice and was greatly discouraged by his slow progress and depressed by his condition as a whole.

The dispensary patient, hearing Mr. Tate's record, volunteered the statement: "That man would do a lot better if he came to class, because we talk to one another and exchange feelings." This indicates that the patients themselves are aware of the advantages of the group approach.

Until the last decade, there was a tendency to regard Group Therapy as "unscientific" and "empirical," the latter term being applied with a subtly derogatory connotation. In the last few years there has been a distinct change in this attitude, and the war especially has emphasized it. Several factors appear to be responsible for the greater recognition that the group approach is now receiving. Obviously, one of these factors is the greater demand for psychotherapy and the necessity for developing some technique that will enable psychiatrics to meet this demand with the comparatively limited equipment and trained personnel at its command. Also, it has undoubtedly been recognized that individual therapy is not in itself sufficient in some cases; in certain instances insight without some framework of support, such as Group Psychotherapy provides, might conceivably even have detrimental results. Furthermore, group psychotherapy has had notable success in certain conditions in which individual therapy has been tried with very limited results. This is strikingly true in the treatment of stuttering.

In treating stuttering, the most obvious advantages are the following:

1. Group Therapy gives the stutterer an opportunity to act against his symptom in the situation that ordinarily provokes it. By adroit management, environmental pressure can be sufficiently lessened to assure success at the outset of treatment and can be gradually increased as the patient progresses.

2. Since everyone in the group has the same difficulties and essentially the same conflicts, problems and general personality traits, the individual comes to identify himself with his fellow

patients. This serves to break down narcissistic barriers and therefore makes the patient more accessible to psychotherapy.

3. Group Therapy removes much of the resistance to insight. The individual is much more willing to recognize his own limitations and conflicts when he realizes that he shares them with his fellow patients. Often he comes to appreciate the existence in himself of certain characteristics through having first recognized them in someone else. Thus he gains insight both directly and indirectly.

4. Because Group Therapy ordinarily lessens resistance to insight, the patient can usually be "pushed" to a greater extent than in individual treatment; in this respect group psychotherapy in the future may possibly be found to provide (in many cases) a less time-consuming technique than individual psychotherapy.

5. Group treatment, if properly organized, gives the patient valuable support and provides him with a framework in which he can apply his gradually gained insight.

6. The individual patient is much more likely to persist with therapy when he is part of a group and when he sees, in the progress that more advanced patients have made, the value of continuing treatment.

Experience with speech sufferers, which perhaps may not be equally applicable to other groups, focuses attention upon a number of important points that must be considered in planning therapy groups. Some of these follow:

1. The therapist should be chosen with discrimination. He should be psychologically oriented, but at the same time he must not be so rigidly circumscribed by his psychological training that he cannot adapt himself to ideas and procedures that may differ from the generally accepted views. He must bring to his task, in addition to training, a good deal of intuitive understanding. In working with stutterers, it has been found that the best therapists are those who have been speech sufferers themselves and have worked their own problems through successfully.

2. The therapist should not discriminate between patients by showing likes or dislikes and should be completely accepting in the earlier stages of treatment. In the later stages, he may call

attention to shortcomings and unhealthy personality traits and reactions; but at no stage should he withdraw approval from the person himself.

3. The therapist should never use his leadership to force patients into a situation where they may feel themselves in an inferior position. Schilder, emphasizing this point, stated: [14] "The fundamental equality of the physician (therapist) with any one member of the group, and the equality of members of the group should be stressed."

4. Patients in any one group should present problems that are essentially similar and should be in the same general phase of treatment. There are, however, certain circumstances in which it is therapeutically advantageous to bring patients in the first stage of treatment in contact with others who are more advanced.

5. In the course of treatment, patients should be exposed to several different therapists and several groups. This furnishes opportunities for ever widening adjustments. If possible, the groups should be graduated in size, so that the new patient is placed in a smaller group and progresses to increasingly larger ones.

6. The therapist should be acquainted with the individual patient's history and background so that he will be aware of the specific needs of each person and can take them into consideration in directing group discussion and activity.

7. The therapist should re-state frequently the basic goal of therapy: that the aim is to treat the personality as a whole and not the symptom.

8. The therapist should be easily available for private discussion of individual problems. Psychiatric assistance should also be available.

9. The group should meet frequently, if possible, several times a week. Otherwise the patient may lose much of the ground gained in the group sessions.

10. There should be a variety of supportive group activities to supplement the actual therapeutic sessions.

[14] *loc. cit.*

Chapter Ten

INTERVIEW GROUP THERAPY WITH A NEUROTIC ADOLESCENT GIRL SUFFERING FROM CHOREA

In this chapter is given a condensed version of the treatment of one girl by group interview technique. The group consisted at varying times from eight to six girls, all of whom were psychoneurotic and presented particularly difficult problems, both in social and intrapsychic adjustment. The neuroses in some of these girls were superimposed upon infantile character, latent schizophrenic trends and similar serious difficulties. All members of the group had been under individual treatment anywhere from six months to two years with the same therapist that conducted the group.

Group treatment was indicated for these girls because some of them proved unable to gain from individual psychotherapy. Some were too resistive to treatment because they were suspicious and distrustful of adults; the ego defenses of others were too strong to venture forth and reveal themselves to a case worker, who saw them on a one-hour-a-week basis. Some were considered to need group treatment because of their retardation in general development and their need for experience and association with girls of their own age with whom they could identify and after whom they could model their own behavior and attitudes. For several, the individual treatment situation was too artificial. It was felt that they would respond better to the reality of group relationships. All the girls resisted individual treatment to varying degrees and the resistances were greatly diminished through the catalytic effect of the group.

The case presented in this chapter was selected largely because of the dramatic quality of the improvement, and because it boldly illustrates some of the basic dynamics in Interview Group Therapy. Among these are the breaking down of the ego defenses the girl had built up against revealing the asocial nature of her family, particularly of her father; the transfer of her psychic energy from its anchorage in her father to the therapist, and the social maturity the group facilitated in this patient.*

Lillie Stone, I.Q. 94, was referred for treatment in November of 1942, at the age of thirteen-and-a-half years, by a family agency. Placement had been recommended by a hospital, where she was treated for Sydenham's Chorea; but neither the mother nor Lillie were willing to accept the plan. Lillie disliked social workers because of unpleasant experiences with them and refused to accept treatment. She was, however, willing to join a club if one were available.

Mrs. Stone, somewhat older than her husband, was neat and of slight build. She had a hearing defect and spoke in a high-pitched, thin, demanding tone of voice. She was anxious and harassed and wept readily. Mrs. Stone spoke of herself as having been a "slave" to her mother who, however, loved the youngest of her eight children most.

Mrs. Stone described Lillie as a sensitive, moody, depressed girl, shy and withdrawn, whose tics included bizarre facial grimaces, constant movement of lips, head jerk and involuntary shuffling of feet. Lillie had presented problems since the age of six. She stayed home from school on the slightest pretext, had no friends and was constantly near her mother. Lillie complained incessantly and the mother, in sheer desperation, decided that she would either "kill or cure" her daughter. There was intense rivalry between Lillie and her sister, Gladys, two years older. Gladys wanted Lillie out of the home.

Mr. Stone was a robust man, in his middle thirties. He had

---

* For a further discussion of the dynamics of Interview Group Therapy see Chapters One and Seven. See also Rhea, Chapter Four, pp. 91 *et seq.*, who was a member of this group.

been one of five siblings, of a poor, sloppy, dirty home. He was infantile and demanding, strutted and dressed flashily. For fifteen years he had worked nights as a taxi driver, sleeping during the day, and always disinclined to work in bad weather. He yelled and banged the furniture and hurled shoes when his sleep was disturbed. He raided the ice box regularly, and ate all the food leaving none for the children or his wife. He was either "silly or moody," and alternatingly behaved seductively toward his daughters, or deprived them of the necessities of life.

Mr. Stone blamed the mother for Lillie's illnesses because, according to him, she nagged the girl, was quick tempered and rejecting. He considered his wife selfish and demanding and thought that when she married him, she married a "meal ticket." He was devoted to Lillie, and catered to her at times, but he recalled that he once slapped her severely at the age of seven, when she resisted dental treatment. The marital tension in the home was so great that he had a "near nervous breakdown" when Lillie was about eleven years old. He grew very weak, was unable to stand up or to work. He was aware that his illness was caused by emotional stress. He described his wife as domineering, strong and unsympathetic. He had been on the verge of suicide a number of times.

When first seen, Lillie appeared older than her thirteen-and-a-half years. She was tall and well built. She appeared depressed, spoke in a monotone, and in an apathetic manner. One of her striking characteristics was complete affectlessness of her face. It was devoid of expression. She was distrustful and wary. In the hospital they asked her "crazy questions" about her family background and parents. She wanted friends, she said, but she felt that she was only tolerated by people and most often left out of things. She considered herself inferior because she was not up to grade in school on account of illnesses. She hated being called "Daddy Long Legs" (she was 5' 7" tall), she hated her name and deplored having to "hang on the tail" of her sister. She also daydreamed and stared into space until she got dizzy and her eyes blurred. She said when she was a small child she had dreamed of dragons and snakes, and she had nightmares of a snake crawling on her. At other times the dragon seemed to lift her high into the air. Now that she was older, she dreamed of boys and dates.

Lillie felt that her mother always criticized her and compared her unfavorably to other girls and to Gladys, who was more outgoing. The mother nagged her endlessly because of her tics of which, Lillie stated, she herself was not aware. Lillie bitterly complained about the quarrels between her mother and father and of her mother's slapping the girls at the slightest provocation. The scenes depressed Lillie and made her "nervous." She felt her father loved her but he too either petted her and gave her "bear hugs" and money, or he neglected her completely. This inconsistency disturbed her.

Lillie described their home as a "miserable place". Beds and chairs were tied with rope to hold them together and visitors were unwelcome because the family was ashamed of the home. There was never enough money for household needs or clothes and whichever way she turned, she felt "frustrated." She occasionally truanted because she was afraid there would be a fight at home in her absence.

Gladys was a buxom, "earthy" type of child. She was boisterous, loud, demanding and attention getting. She was hostile to Lillie in revenge for Lillie's domination through her illnesses. At nineteen, Gladys still had no boy friends. The mother stated that Gladys was like her father. Both were shallow but made friends easily.

Lillie was an unwanted child and presented many difficulties in her development. Dentition started at six months with temperatures up to 105 degrees each time she cut a tooth. She had measles and chicken pox at five years, and a tonsillectomy at seven. She entered school at six years of age. At seven years she fell down frequently. She slept in the parents' bedroom most of the time until she reached her thirteenth year.

The choreiform movements which were finally diagnosed as Sydenham's Chorea, began in the seventh year of her life. When the family visited her in the hospital the tics became more pronounced and subsided when the family left. At the hospital Lillie resisted treatment, was extremely shy and withdrawn, and rejected all relationships. A stay in a convalescent home followed. On being discharged from convalescence, the hospital plan was to place this child away from her home, but Lillie refused to leave.

Sydenham's Chorea is generally regarded by neurologists as a form of toxic encephalopathy, of more or less specific type, but its anatomical basis is still unclear. Some children who have been subject to attacks of chorea subsequently show a tendency to react by choreic movements to any nervous strain later in life, or may exhibit a habitual motor unrest. Two possible explanations may be advanced for this tendency: that the movements have become habitual by constant repetition or that the disease may have resulted in a mild but permanent injury to the brain.

It was recognized that Lillie's pathological home environment was an important factor in the aggravation and maintenance of her choreic symptoms and she was referred to the Jewish Board of Guardians .

When Lillie first came for treatment she had in a large measure recovered from one or more acute attacks of Sydenham's Chorea. But she found it difficult to express her emotions either through language or in other voluntary motor activity. Much of her energy was being discharged in the form of hysterical symptoms: choreic movements, depression, dizziness, blurring of vision, shyness, tendency to withdraw from relationships. The diagnosis most consistent with the clinical picture was hysteria (mixed psychoneurosis) with depression, conversion and withdrawal symptoms.

All this served as an expression of hostile feelings against her parents and sister, and as a form of revenge for the frustrations that she suffered at their hands. She needed her relatives too much to express her hostile feelings to them, so she took it out on herself in the form of hysterical symptoms. A secondary gain of these symptoms was that she disturbed her relatives and all the people with whom she came into contact, and elicited attention from them.

For two years Lillie was treated in individual interviews by a psychiatric caseworker. She expressed distrust of people. She could not forget that at one time, secrets she had told to a friend had been divulged, and now she feared attachments. It was for this reason that she preferred a club. She consistently resisted coming to see the case worker and missed many appointments.

As time progressed and she became a little more communicative, she related the following incident: a few weeks before she had attended a party; at 11 P. M. her mother had called for her and beaten her in the presence of the guests. She did not speak to the family for two days, but expressed sympathy for her mother, whom she described as a quiet and introverted person who did not go out much.

Lillie spoke of having had many injections, which made her drowsy, dizzy and nauseated. Once after an injection treatment, she was alone in the house and felt violently ill; she thought she would die and imagined the doctors had given her an overdose. From then on, she was convinced the injections remained in her. She suffered from dryness of the throat and for relief drank a great deal of water. She hated school, because she was always told there what to do. She was unable to express anger against her mother and so she threw things at her sister instead.

Despite these occasional confidences, Lillie continued to resist treatment just as she had at the hospital. She did not keep her appointments with the case worker and was given three months to decide whether or not she wanted to continue. She now began to keep appointments fairly regularly. As a part of the treatment plan, the worker introduced her to a club at a settlement house. There she competed for the first time successfully with her older sister, who also joined because Lillie attracted the boys and Gladys wanted to benefit by this.

After six months Lillie became more communicative in treatment. She no longer talked about her father as someone to have fun with, but instead began to criticize him as a grouch, who disrupted the household and was selfish. She complained of getting dizzy spells and headaches in school. We sent her to an eye specialist and with a change of glasses this condition improved.

Gladys' sixteenth birthday went unnoticed by the father but the following week he gave Lillie a fountain pen for her birthday. She also got other gifts but lost all of them. She felt sorry for Gladys for having been neglected and criticized her father for his behavior and irresponsibility.

After seven months of treatment the mother still complained of the recurrence of Lillie's symptoms. Mrs. Stone confided that the girl had been receiving chiropractic treatments which she was keeping a secret from the worker. The agency psychiatrist suggested that Lillie give up all other treatment and that she be helped to disclose the "secret" to the case worker.

At this time Lillie also expressed resentment of her mother's lack of understanding. Her mother had been beating her, expecting her to control her involuntary movements. The caseworker helped Lillie to reveal her secret and to give up all other forms of treatment. There was an exacerbation of the choreiform movements and a neurological examination was arranged. The neurologist found that the exacerbation of the symptoms was of hysterical origin. Lillie's resentment of the neurological examination and possibly of the worker's part in it, coupled with the family's financial stress at this time, were reflected in a regression of her condition. Moreover she also fell down stairs at the settlement house in her excitement over speaking with a boy. Her mother therefore forbade her to attend the club.

Two months later, as conditions in the home improved and she was getting on better with Gladys, Lillie's choreiform movements decreased. Her general health improved and she gained weight. She began to have some insight into her problem and asked for advice on planning her high school studies. It was suggested that a psychological examination would help. She readily agreed.

The psychologist found Lillie's manner self-effacing and apprehensive. She was cooperative and appeared gratified by the personal attention she was receiving. The results of the psychometric test placed her in the average range of intelligence. Her achievement level was slightly retarded. A commercial course was recommended as the most suitable vocational program.

At this time the girl was also given the first of three Rorschach examinations. Her responses to the test material revealed a seriously disturbed adolescent, who was very agitated by the blots, and was afraid to extend herself. She continually requested assurance and guidance from the examiner and offered many qualifications and apologies.

The girl suffered from extreme feelings of personal worthlessness and inner disharmony. She felt helpless and had catastrophic fears of injury and abandonment. Her preoccupation with the gloomy dysphoric qualities of the blots suggested periods of depression and brooding which seemed linked to her feelings of inferiority and frustration. The test showed that although socially isolated and withdrawn, she was eager for attachments to people and longed for emotional closeness. Her fear of social ties seemed related to a fear of retaliation and rejection. She was intimidated by her own aggressive tendencies which prevented her from discharging hostile impulses through normal channels and seemed to direct her aggression inward.

The girl seemed suggestible, easily swayed and showed a proneness to loose, uncontrolled behavior. This tendency to primitive, emotional response in conjunction with a preoccupation with her body was highly suggestive of symptoms of conversion hysteria.

The Rorschach gave a graphic picture of the girl's disturbed sexuality. She was extremely disturbed by the sexual implications in the blots and her many transparent responses and thinly veiled projections in this area made it unlikely that she was merely exhibiting a normal adolescent curiosity. Her frequent and concrete allusions to erotic symbols, to dragons and phallic configurations and her anal preoccupation seemed not only a product of her fantasy life, but of a traumatizing sexual experience. On one card she saw a phallic symbol to which she responded in an evasive manner and then continued with a description of a threatening "gorilla, surrounded by blood stains." The sexual inferences were striking and sophisticated. It was not unlikely that the girl's relationship with her father may have contained some traumatic elements.

In the intellectual sphere, she displayed at least average capacities, which were used fairly adequately, although she seemed capable of functioning on an even higher plane. On the whole, her intellectual functioning was not as seriously interfered with as her emotional functioning. She showed some disinclination to think along the lines of other girls of her age, and encountered difficulty in adjusting to the practical requirements of life. The diagnostic impressions of the first Rorschach confirmed the psychiatric diagnosis of a psychoneurosis with predominant conversion hysteria and depressive features. The prognosis seemed favorable on the basis of the girl's capacity for insight, for establishing emotional relationships, and of her desire for help.

After eight months of individual treatment Lillie was again sent to a psychiatrist because the choreiform movements continued, probably because of her hatred of doctors and her anger against the caseworker. The old tensions seemed re-awakened, and mouth movements and twisting of the tongue became more pronounced. Shortly thereafter, Lillie became ill with a temperature of 102 degrees. The family physician diagnosed the attack as acute appendicitis and suggested surgery. The caseworker's suspicion of a conversion symptom was confirmed by a diagnostician on the agency's staff. His findings were negative. This was discussed with Lillie and it was interpreted as a manifestation of physical symptoms in her attempt to control a situation and to get her revenge. She admitted that she had over-eaten and that she did not want to go to school.

Another way Lillie used to gain her own ends was by going to sleep. When she awoke, she was glum, moody and unhappy. The worker told Lillie that it lay within her power to get well. Lillie spontaneously replied: "I know it to be the truth." When Mrs. Stone insisted that Lillie go to camp for the summer, the girl's reaction to this was: "They want to get rid of me." The mother's purpose was to get Lillie away from the father's seductive attempts to which she now attributed much of Lillie's illness. She succeeded in her efforts to get Lillie away to camp.

When Lillie returned to school in the fall of 1943 she had a severe attack of hay fever. Injections were recommended, but she preferred to "suffer." She now enjoyed school because her teachers were "intelligent, younger, and more competent" than her previous teachers. The family situation improved greatly at this time; the house was refurnished. The family entertained guests at home and Gladys and Lillie brought their friends. Lillie was now able to criticize her father more freely and expressed sympathy for her mother, who was being deprived because the father selfishly indulged himself. Lillie vehemently remarked that she would not marry such a man, and if she were to marry such a man, she would handle him differently from the way her mother had.

At this time, Lillie began to think of her future. She wanted to grow into maturity and resented it that her parents still treated her as a child. She no longer indulged in daydreaming; she was too busy for that. The dryness of the mouth disappeared from talking with her caseworker, she said. From her biology studies she learned that the injections that had so upset her in the past must have been absorbed long ago. She wondered what made her think that they could have stayed in her. The worker clarified this by explaining the sexual symbolism of the injections. However, when sexual material was brought out, Lillie became inordinately embarrassed, though she did admit that she masturbated.

Later in the winter of 1943, Lillie began to dress nicely and she looked more attractive. She was still conflicted about her father. When she complained of feeling tired and in need of a rest, as it was difficult for her to get up in the morning for school, this was discussed with her in terms of her habit of fleeing into illness as a means of protection, of revenge and as an expression of her hostility. Lillie was able to tie up her feeling of debility with her feelings about her father. As she put it: "He is still up to his old tricks." When the family talked seriously to him, he turned everything into a joke. She wanted her father to consider her as a grown-up person, and not as a baby. However, she no longer gave in to her impulse to stay in bed rather than to go to school.

When sex was again introduced, Lillie revealed that she feared going to parties because it meant getting into contact with boys.

During this period Mrs. Stone was seen by the case worker about once a month. She seemed to get a great deal of comfort from these talks and often said they kept her from exploding. She recognized considerable improvement in Lillie, particularly that she was more quiet. The twitchings or jerky movements had disappeared except when company was present. Lillie had made some friends. However, there was the fear ever present in the mother that Lillie would lose her friends because she was a "sour puss." There was some basis for this fear, since Lillie had not yet improved enough. There was still some facial immobility and her voice was still colorless. Lillie now competed with Gladys and tried to take away her sister's boy friends. When Mrs. Stone pointed out to Lillie that she competed with Gladys, Lillie absent-mindedly cut up the handle of a knife she was holding, with another knife.

After one-and-a-half years it was observed that Lillie developed hives and one of her hips began to protrude. Our staff physician diagnosed a spinal curvature and recommended treatment.

Continued improvement in Lillie's behavior was noted. She spoke more freely in interviews. She became more alert. She was made an usher during graduating exercises at school. Gladys, who had graduated from school previously, was now working and gave Lillie a regular weekly allowance. Lillie was reaching out for social contacts. In school she no longer felt that her lessons were difficult and she insisted on taking a part time job, in spite of her mother's refusal to permit her to work. This was the first time Lillie openly defied her mother. Yet, though Lillie felt more comfortable now, she revealed that she had always feared the dark. She knew it was silly, yet there was in her the feeling that "in the dark she could be attacked."

However, despite her efforts, Lillie had not succeeded in forming friendships. She did join several clubs at various centers and at the homes of some of the girls she knew, but she did not really feel at ease. Invariably she made some excuse for discontinuing her associations. She still moved her tongue and rolled her eyes when unhappy. She realized that the tongue movements had something to do with her fantasy of wanting to be kissed. She was preoccupied with thoughts of social engagements and of boy friends.

Briefly, Lillie had responded to individual treatment with considerable reserve. While she had become able to give up some of her physical symptoms when not under strain in the home, the symptoms reappeared as soon as the family situation was again disturbed. She had gained considerable release from treatment in the individual interviews, but she had dealt only with superficial matters and protected herself from revealing the depth of her problem. It seemed that a strong repressed hostility to the mother had made it impossible to develop a close relationship with the worker which would have permitted her to reach toward the center of her difficulties, namely her involvement with her father.

Summing up the treatment to this point: the caseworker helped the girl to understand that by her grimacing and choreiform movements she not only was expressing her hostility to her mother, but that she was in turn also stimulating her mother's hostility to herself. Lillie was helped to verbalize her hostility to her father by complaining about him. She was evidently convinced that she had been made ill by the physicians as she had been by her father. She attributed to them her own fears of her father's incestuous tendencies. Therefore she felt that the typhoid vaccine injections had made her worse. To her they appeared to represent sexual intercourse.

She apparently developed fantasies of being pregnant and was fearful of this imagined pregnancy. The fantasies were repressed but they appeared in her symptoms. She felt that she had received an overdose of an injection from a doctor and that this injection was lodged and stayed within her. She tried to restrain her desire to wiggle her hips and attract men; instead she developed the symptom of a protruding hip, also suggestive of a protruding pregnancy. She tried not to reveal that she felt herself to be a fallen girl or one that wanted to fall for men. Instead, she had to act out this fantasy and fell down repeatedly. By falling she punished herself for her sexual desires. Her hives and her excessive thirst had a similar unconscious content: reactions to and punishment for her fantasied pregnancy. She was eventually able to state that she would have been a better mother than her own mother and would have made her father a better wife. She began to release some hostile feelings to her mother and sister. She now talked back to her mother and told both of them she resented their domination. She learned to verbalize her resentments with her case worker, who quietly accepted her expressions of hostility. In this way, Lillie became less afraid of her own hostility and thus less dependent. In putting more energy for other activities at her disposal, the emotional release made it possible for her to improve.

She dressed better, became more outgoing and began to develop friendships with some girls as her hostility to her mother and sister decreased. However, she was still very much blocked by her fear of her mother and this blocking resulted in the retention of some symptoms, primarily grimacing and tongue movements which were connected with her fantasies of conception through the mouth.

During the course of treatment there were several regressions and they were precipitated by traumatic factors in the home and/or the occurrence of insurmountable resistances in the transference situation with the worker. The latter proved too difficult to resolve at that stage of individual therapy. On account of the basic resistance the girl had against the worker, as a mother figure, dilution of the relationship seemed indicated, into one that would be less threatening. Therefore group treatment was recommended.

It must be noted that the girl herself had a deep desire for social relationships. This was evidenced by the fact that Lillie on her own joined a number of groups, which was interpreted as her wish to find a more satisfactory family than hers was. The group also supplied a situation analogous to her family.

After two years of individual psychotherapy, group treatment was introduced. Lillie was prepared for and introduced to a group consisting of five other girls, in February 1944. Individual treatment was discontinued. All the girls had been in individual treatment and the same worker was also the therapist of the group.

The girls had been invited to a party and as they were eating ice cream and cake, one of the girls remarked that it reminded her of parties in her garden when she was a little girl in Europe. This stimulated all to talk of incidents in their early lives, particularly when they played with dolls. The therapist sensed that they were revealing basic problems in the way they used their dolls and the content of the play episodes was interpreted to the girls as indicative of some of their early difficulties. The therapist also suggested that in this group they could talk of whatever came to their minds.

Lillie attended practically every session, though it often involved considerable hardship for her. During the first ten sessions she said nothing. She just listened. When the therapist asked Lillie's opinion on what had been said, Lillie would reply in a monosyllable, "yes" or "no." The first active response from Lillie was elicited by a discussion on the spending of money. Lillie spontaneously said that she had been a hoarder, but that she now changed.

When the subject of fathers came up during the early sessions, Lillie's reserve was even more pronounced. She described her father as the ideal parent. The other occasional comments she was able to make during this period were in the nature of giving advice and in pointing out that some of the girls were unable to express their thoughts.

An incestuous sexual dream related by one of the girls caused Lillie evident annoyance. She refused to listen to it and at the next session she grimaced and blew her nose continuously, which irritated the girls. They told her to get treatment for her nasal condition. Because of this she withdrew into herself for the next few sessions. Lillie's feelings about sex were also demonstrated when marriage was discussed by the other girls. She said she was not ready to join in such a discussion; it reminded her, she said, of a "childish girl I knew who could not go on dates without a chaperon." When one of the girls read excerpts from a book on the subject, Lillie pointed out that the reader's hand shook.

However, later Lillie participated more easily again in the discussions. Her appearance also improved noticeably and the girls commented on it. Lillie now became really a part of the group and she almost apologetically remarked that she had had difficulty in discussing her problems in the past, but as she had listened to the other girls, she was becoming aware of participating in the conversations to an extent never before experienced, and she added: "Each week that I come here makes me more secure to express myself. I lost my inhibitions by coming to this club."

At about the fiftieth session, it was noticed that Lillie was able to take part in discussions that touched on areas in which she already felt some security. She seemed to understand herself better. She said that formerly she was quiet, unhappy and morose. Her mother had complained that she never smiled. "Now I feel free and ready to enjoy my life." She added: "Here we get sociable and we learn how to act with different people. We get something off our chests while we are having a good time." She stopped completely rolling her eyes, but she still twitched her mouth occasionally. She was still given to moodiness but less frequently and the moods were of shorter duration.

When sex was discussed and suspicion was cast on one of the girls regarding her activities with her boy friend, Lillie seemed more tolerant as she remarked: "We are here to say what is on our minds." It was at this point that she had her first date and that she requested an individual interview with the group therapist. She was anxious about the fact that the boy she had gone out with had kissed and petted her. After talking about it with the therapist, she was able to bring her problem for discussion in the group.

During the winter of 1945, Lillie entered a new phase. She criticized parents, stating that the behavior of children reflected the way the parents have brought them up. She also remarked on the manner in which mothers tend to dominate their children, causing them to remain emotionally immature.

When the subject of friends came up, Lillie identified with the quiet girls in the group, but she was able to realize that it was necessary to reach out for friends, else one would never have any. She commented as follows: "Actually I never had a real childhood because I did not play with little girls. I lived so much in myself. I was never able to pretend playing house." She thought that was why her maturity was retarded. Sometimes she thought she would still like to recapture some childhood days, she had felt so frustrated and unhappy as a child, she would like to relive happier days. The other girls, in responding to Lillie's statement, also felt they had lost out on some of the play that is normal for children. Thus they all identified with each other.

A Tree Grows in Brooklyn was brought in by Lillie, who was impressed with Francine's mother. The question was raised: "What happens when a girl becomes devirginized?" Considerable thought was given to the mother's role toward her daughter. They tried to evaluate how Francie would have felt had she given herself to the soldier. Lillie said she would have been mortified if she had been deserted by the man, and she would never have trusted a man the rest of her life. She asked the girls' advice as to whether she should go out with a boy somewhat younger and inexperienced with girls. They told her to go with him and weeks later, when the same discussion came up, the girls told her that she likes boys younger than herself because her father is a young looking man.

A second Rorschach was administered one year after the first to evaluate Lillie's progress. The results reflected the girl's improvement in both her intellectual and emotional functioning.

She was less agitated and less anxious. She still needed assurance, but she was not as evasive and fearful as she had been on the previous test. She was more self-reliant, had personal pride and showed more realistic conformity strivings as noted in her use of more commonplace concepts. It was anticipated that she would be less fearful of indulging in activities usually associated with girls of her age. In contrast with the earlier test, the girl also showed an increasing awareness of her feminine role. She made tentative references to articles of personal adornment and clothes, which had been entirely absent in the previous test.

Perhaps the most marked gain made over the year was the lessening of her overexcitability to the emotional impact of her environment. This was a distinct contrast to her earlier surrender to the colored, that is affect-awakening, stimuli in the blots. She was still inclined to be impulsive but was beginning to show greater flexibility and genuine spontaneity in her emotional response.

Her sexual preoccupation remained a conspicuous feature in her responses. Her preoccupation with erotic symbols and anal material, although still present, had diminished. The earlier frightening "blood stains" and "gorrilla" seen on a card usually associated with the parental figures, now gave way to a more acceptable response which suggested the lessening of the effects of the earlier traumatizing experience. The girl was still presenting a serious disturbance in this area and showed considerable blocking which probably prevented her from discussing these problems. There were also indications of conflict and guilt about masturbatory activity, which she seemed unable to bring into the open.

Although there were still many evidences of intrapsychic constriction, the girl was showing greater freedom and richness in her productivity. She manifested improvement in the direction of greater emotional stability, organization, discipline and control. She indicated many gains in her personality structure but she still was far from being a well adjusted adolescent. However, she was moving in a positive direction and the possible prognosis seemed very promising.

By this time Lillie had gained considerable security. Through the group discussion she had been helped to understand her conflicts and she now openly criticized her home as a "madhouse." She wondered as to how she ought to react to the quarrels at home; she said she generally took sides with her father. She said: "You wash your hands, but what's the use, they'll only get dirty again." By this she meant to convey that there seemed no end to the difficulties at home. She wondered whether people who do nice things mostly expect something in return. The group disagreed with her. Some of the girls said: "It's the way you do a thing, and the spirit you put into it that counts."

Lillie then spoke of her parents as having queer ideas about life. They did not talk with their children about sex and "the facts of life." Whenever the subject came up, they treated it as though there was something mysterious about it. The therapist explained that formerly our parents were not brought up to talk of these things. Lillie believed that if parents would talk frankly with their children when they are young, it would avoid embarrassing moments later on. An example was given by one of the girls who then advocated that petting should be indulged in, especially "if you feel that you are in love." Lillie considered this the wrong way to win a man. There followed a discussion about delinquency which the girls attempted to define; they were stimulated to think and to talk about the whole problem from the point of view of the influences the family environment has on a child's life.

An animated discussion of behavior patterns, standards and morals of the group followed. As a result, one of the girls wrote a love story in which she described herself as infantile, underdeveloped, and as having a deep inferiority feeling. Her mother had to become a matchmaker. Lillie laughingly commented that she wished her mother was a successful matchmaker. They pondered on why beautiful women so often marry unattractive men. Lillie agreed with one of the girls who suggested that there was fear of competition. Lillie added that her father was "in his second childhood." Spontaneously, one of the girls asked Lillie why she went out with a boy younger than herself. Lillie said she was giving him up; he was too infantile, too young.

At one of the sessions the subject of death came up and Lillie said she thought of death as of something that would be coming to her sometime, but she put it off as she thought of all the things she would miss if she were dead. She was particularly intrigued with all the modern things that are being developed in this age. She would like to be here to profit from all the changes as they take place. One of the girls asked whether she would like to return one hundred years from now; another question she was thinking about was "suspended animation." At this period there developed considerable discussion which seemed to relate to birth. A brief example will have to suffice. They spoke of fear of being covered over during sleep, of fears of choking and dying in their sleep. The therapist interpreted to them that their fears stemmed from the unconscious, since they had to do with some early fears that they were yet unaware of.

In June 1945 the girls discussed "culture" as a general subject and topics that concerned them greatly were music, good plays, good books, and so forth. What disturbed them was that so often, as portrayed in the theatre, people with culture have murderous instincts. They had seen the play called *Arsenic and Old Lace*. The question was raised as to how vital in life was the element of fanaticism. Lillie frankly stated that she had never given these things any thought until she heard the discussions here. At about this time Lillie began going to concerts.

The subject of fathers was now probed but more deeply than before. Lillie demonstrated the new security she had gained when she discussed her father in terms of his real character. During an argument with Mrs. Stone over his maiden sister, Mrs. Stone threatened to leave home if his sister moved in with them. Mr. Stone said he could always get another wife, but not another sister. Lillie described him as selfish and egotistical, moody, and though he started quarrels, he would afterwards stop talking to the entire family. This made Lillie become depressed. The girls recognized Lillie's sadness and talked about it, pointing out to her that the quarrels between her parents should not concern her. They also made her aware of her hidden sympathy for her father at these times. Lillie smiled self-consciously when it was first pointed out to her that she was not so kind to her mother. At a later meeting she told the group that she had examined her own feelings and she had come to the conclusion that the girls were right.

Another topic explored was why parents did not place confidence and trust in their children. Lillie thought there might be something within the parents that caused them to act like that.

A book report written by one of the girls, and read to the group, was concerned with the problem of how to attain maturity. Laughingly, one of the girls said they should feel competent to discuss this topic, since they were adolescents and adolescence is the bridge that connects childhood with maturity. Lillie questioned whether in this modern environment young people receive sufficient stimulus to grow up because so much is done for them. Spontaneously, all entered into a game, as it were, of enumerating all the things people of another century had to do for themselves to achieve some degree of comfort. Thus they were forced to invent things. They spoke of the days when people rubbed flint to obtain light, while today one only has to push a button. When it was felt they had exhausted the problem, Lillie refused to stop. She said there was still a need to discuss the growing-up process. The question of sex again came up especially whether a girl should "give in" if she was being driven nearly crazy with passion. Lillie could not believe that an inexperienced girl could have such a strong sexual urge. With an air of finality, she said: "It can be overcome."

Again Lillie expressed the thought that most parents were unable to properly influence their offspring and when the therapist gave the girls a brief talk about early training and upbringing of an infant, such as would lead to a feeling of security and confidence toward the parents, there was unanimous agreement when one of the girls fervently said: "Thank God we will be better mothers than ours were."

In January of 1946 there was a short period of regression on

Lillie's part; a recurrence of the shuffling of her feet and some nervous tension was noted, but there were no choreiform movements. One of the girls was displaying aggression toward the therapist. Lillie identified with the girl by acting up, laughing and disrupting the session. However, she returned at the next session feeling quite guilty about her behavior. She denied she was angry.at the therapist who gave some interpretation of the aggressive and hostile feelings expressed, and also questioned whether Lillie's reactions had resulted from tensions generated in the group during the discussions on marriage, sex, birth, and so forth. One of the girls explained to Lillie that things had been "tight" in her and that in the group she had opened up and had spoken about whatever was in her mind. The girl advised Lillie to continue to do this, because she could feel secure with all of them. Lillie became even more talkative and related that she had become intoxicated at a party where she drank champagne for the first time. She now asked why people take liquor to excess when it knocks them out. The interpretation was given and accepted that drinking was a means of ridding oneself and each other of inhibitions.

At another session Lillie, while listening to the girls, wrote out two pages of complaints about her family situation, and especially about her father's behavior. She said he had fooled around with her and now had turned against her and did not even speak to her. The therapist wondered whether her father's attitude might not have to do with his realization of her growing maturity. He was trying to adapt himself to it. The girls were doodling and one remarked that from the picture Lillie made, it looked as though she feared to have unconscious things come through. At the next session Lillie seemed much happier and looked radiant. The girls remarked on it to her.

Lillie had not been seen in individual interviews for two-and-a-half years. At this time, in the middle of 1946, an incident that occurred in the group, prompted one of the members to tell that she had killed a cat following a quarrel with her boy friend. All the girls in the group were disturbed over this and the discussion that followed. All the girls requested individual interviews with the therapist. During this interview Lillie brought out considerable feeling against her father and her sister. She also stated she now would like to work in a hospital because she herself had not received the treatment she required there.

During the summer of 1946, the group met at the beach in the Stone cottage. Lillie conducted herself as a perfect hostess and this picnic was the forerunner of several more that followed during the summer. In the fall of 1946, the girls talked about the oedipus complex, since one of the girls had been reading a book on psychiatry. Lillie said she had been having some beautiful dreams. She related one. She dreamed that while crossing the street, a small Negro boy became confused when a car suddenly approached. She became "the hero." She jumped on him to save his life. Her legs were injured. She became unconscious. When she came to, she was in the hospital. A young Jewish physician attended her daily. After two years the time came for her to walk. She felt insecure but was encouraged by the doctor as he stood before her with outstretched arms. She walked haltingly, taking only a few steps, and she weakly fell into his arms. She seemed to be still enjoying the effects of this dream, but was interrupted by the girls who said she was having a fantasy and not a dream. They asked had she been fully asleep? Lillie laughed and said it might have been a continuous fantasy, to which the girls replied that Lillie wanted to get married.

A third Rorschach given at that time, two years after the second and three years after the first test, revealed considerable growth in Lillie's adjustment. Changes that were hinted at in the second test had become crystallized and structuralized. The beginnings of the positive development manifested two years earlier had shown a spontaneous unimpeded growth. The girl's previously constricted, anxiety-ridden reactions gave way to freedom in movement and thought, which was manifested in a rich, productive record. This was a distinct contrast to the meager material and the agitated primitive responses of the first test. A significant modification was seen in her release from the stifling effects of her earlier blocking, which seemed related to greater insight and understanding of her sexual urges.

On the earlier tests she had been reduced to either a rejection of these sexually weighted and anxiety provoking cards, or she resorted to banal non-committal responses which she would not have tolerated if she had been less disturbed in this area. These reactions were considerably diminished in this test. She was able to discharge her hostile impulses in a more normal, direct manner, without the earlier fear of retaliation and rejection. She was now capable of social relations which had more meaning for her, and the earlier indications of isolation and withdrawal occurred only rarely. The increased femininity of her interests was noted in the delicacy and loving devotion with which she described clothes, a subject which now seemed very close to her heart. On the whole, this girl's previous fears of guilt and punishment had been largely dissolved and she seemed released from her debilitating anxieties.

In regard to her sexual development, her preoccupation did not seem to transgress the bounds of adolescent curiosity, but she was still not without difficulties in this area. She had gained considerable insight into the meaning of her sexual drives, but still had many fantasies about intercourse and birth and still tended to relate these phenomena to a fear of physical assault. The earlier gross manifestations had disappeared, the preoccupation with erotic symbols had subsided, and the frightening "blood stains" and other suggestions of defloration were no longer in evidence. However, she still seemed somewhat confused and in need of more reassurance in this area.

A longitudinal study of this girl's response to therapy, as measured by three Rorschach tests, showed gradual and tangible gains. She now appeared to be a fairly well adjusted adolescent in distinct contrast to the initial test picture of a very seriously disturbed, anxious girl with many severe problems.

In evaluating her group experience, Lillie herself stated: "Though I haven't always talked or appeared to be one of the group, I got more here from the discussions than from anything I have ever done in my life. The girls bring in more angles and they help me correct my mistakes." At another time she said to the girls: "Yes, and you never poked fun at me or criticized me, you explained things so that I could understand."

Lillie had overcome her overt symptoms as noted when she first came for treatment. She had not regressed in almost a year, but whenever the parents quarrelled and the father turned away from the family, she grew sad. At such times she brought her problems to the girls. On a number of occasions her strong attachment to her father and her resentment of her mother were pointed out to her as elements in the situation. The girls discussed Lillie's own emotional involvements that caused her to react to or interfere in her parents' quarrels. Lillie generally left such a meeting in a happy frame of mind.

When a school visit was made in October, 1946, the dean of girls was surprised that an inquiry was made about Lillie, as she was one of the "finer girls in the school." She had no difficulties nor did she display tics or bizarre behavior.

Both the mother and father were seen as well. Despite the mother's previous attitude, she had no fault to find with Lillie. She thought that Lillie was beautiful and attractive to boys. She was a conscientious, hard worker. The father, too, could find no fault with Lillie. He expressed his satisfaction with all that had been accomplished with his daughter.

When seen a year after treatment was terminated, when Lillie was about nineteen years old, she was found to have grown very attractive. All symptoms had disappeared. She worked as a secretary in a national organization and was a good worker.

As the mother had predicted a number of times, the father stopped working when the two daughters began to earn good salaries. Lillie talked about this as another symptom of his maladjustment, and as something about which the family could do little. Lillie and her sister maintained the household.

Lillie remained a member of a group of boys and girls in one of the local Y's. She had had one steady boy-friend to whom she was very devoted, but he did not remain as steadfast as Lillie. Lillie was able to accept the loss without too much disturbance.

She had another boy-friend whom she gave up because she felt he was not responsible enough and, therefore, would be a poor risk as a marriage partner. She did not appear disturbed about this either. She said she enjoyed life, saved money, and she seemed to the interviewer generally capable and content.

During the individual treatment Lillie was reaching out for a more satisfactory group setting than the one her home supplied. She had made several attempts on her own to find congenial groups. It was soon evident that she found the therapy group of value. She attended sessions regularly, though her initial response was similar to that in individual therapy. At first she was shy, withdrawn and did not talk. She tried to make a good impression and presented her parents as ideal people.

Lillie was extremely sensitive to disapproval. When blowing her nose displeased the girls, for example, she again became shy and withdrawn and even skipped a few sessions, thus physically removing herself from the situation. At one point she went to the hospital for injections, which suggests that when the girls did not want her, she went to the boys—the doctors—for physical treatment. But when she found that the girls did not really reject her and admitted that they, too, had problems similar to her own, she felt secure and participated more actively in the group. Thus she was helped to identify with other humans and spoke of experiences common to all of them, such as when as children they played with dolls in a garden, their attitudes toward their parents and their fears of sex.

Lillie first reacted to discussions on sex by emphasizing that she was still emotionally dependent and needed a mother figure to help her. But as she began to talk more about her own sexual interest and found that the girls accepted and understood her, she felt freer and began to identify with them. When her new-found freedom extended beyond the therapeutic situation into the outside world, so that she permitted one of her male escorts to pet her, she again became frightened and wanted reassurance from the therapist that she had not done anything wrong. The material suggests that she felt that her mother would disapprove of a physical relationship with a man. She complained that mothers dominated their children and kept them emotionally immature and too dependent.

The more Lillie verbalized her hostility to her mother, the freer did she become in words and actions, which helped her to mature emotionally. She and the other girls began to think of becoming mothers, of being devirginized. She said that if a man devirginized her she would never trust him for the rest of her life. When she came to understand that this terrific fear of being devirginized was tied up with her father and that similar ideas were in the minds of the other girls as well, she grew less fearful of her incest fantasies. Still, she was afraid of her mother's hostility and on occasion her facial grimacing became accentuated. It was soon clear that she hoped to get sympathy from her mother by not expressing in language or action her hostile feelings, but her facial grimacing betrayed how really hostile she felt to her mother.

When she received attention and sympathy in the group and eased her guilt by working hard and talking about it, she was relieved and was able to express her resentment of her home and her family. She resented it that sex had not been discussed frankly in the family the way it had been discussed in the therapy group. She felt reassured when she learned that all mothers did not disapprove of daughters having physical contact with men, that some mothers were actually matchmakers and she wished that her mother had been more aggressive on her daughter's behalf.

Unconsciously, she still feared her mother and therefore inhibited her sexual wishes for her father by permitting herself to think of going out with younger boys. When one of the girls in the group made her aware of this, she expressed a reason for this fear. She spoke of death which she evidently regarded as a condign punishment for incest. She indicated that death and birth were connected in her mind, that she would rather be a child in her mother's womb than be a grown-up woman, in a position to have an incestuous relationship with her father. She was also afraid that she would have to kill her mother or would be killed by her mother if she permitted herself even to think of her wishes for her father.

When Lillie became aware of these conflicts, she was freed to talk of her negative feelings against her father and express her understanding of him. She was able to talk of him as he really was and accept the fact that he was not a wonderful man, as she had imagined him as a child. Her lack of confidence in him had been a factor in preventing her from growing up. She indicated that her father was inconsistent in helping her grow up.

Once she was able to talk about her lack of physical satisfaction from her father, she was also able to think of sexual intercourse between herself and some man. However, she did not feel sufficiently secure in the group setting with this new idea and feeling, and tended to regress. Once the therapist helped her express her feelings of hostility to the group, she was able to talk of her own misbehavior at a party, where she had become drunk, and she was able to talk about her father's advances toward her.

As Lillie learned that she had been afraid of her own incestuous wishes, she began to feel free to think of them with considerably less guilt feelings. When one of the girls spoke of killing a cat, she again tended to regress because it stimulated competitive and murderous impulses against her mother and at this point she again spoke of her resentment of her father. In competition with the father she had vied for her mother's love and vice versa, and had death wishes against her mother in order to get his love.

In the group she gradually began to work toward a healthy attitude toward both parents. She wished them both to live, but here she became aware of her own need to get a man, to get married and to become pregnant, as her mother had, and have a husband of her own.

In summary, then, it can be said that this girl had been inhibited and frustrated by both her parents and by her sister. On the other hand, she had also been overstimulated by her parents. Her mother had had intense outbursts of anger which the girl had come to imitate in facial grimacing. Also, Lillie had expressed her anger in stereotyped, primitive choreiform movements, the only type of which she had been capable at the stage in her development when she was intensely affected by her mother's anger. She had also reacted to her intense feelings against her mother by fear and attempts to run away, and had become shy and withdrawn.

The incestuous stimulation by her father had also motivated her to flee and had aroused fear of death. Her fear of punishment from the mother caused her to repress any action she might take for getting affection from her father and other men. As a result of these frustrations, she withheld her anger, became depressed, and discharged her feelings in choreiform movements. As she began to feel more secure in individual therapy and later in Group Therapy, she was enabled to face her own thoughts and feelings and talk about them. She also was enabled to think and act in a way that made life worthwhile and more pleasant.

In these respects the group was of considerable help. Here Lillie found that girls of her own age had similar ideas and feelings. She was able to accept interpretations she needed in order to understand herself. Not only did the therapist interpret, but the other girls as well did so. In addition, she received attention, felt accepted, and as a result, related to other people in a satisfying manner.

The work with this patient illustrates the advantages of Group Therapy to both patient and therapist. When the individual therapeutic situation entails too difficult an adjustment on the part of the patient, or when the resistances are too strong, the situation can be alleviated by suitable Group Therapy. In the group setting, not only the therapist, but also the other members work on the individual resistances of each; and this is very helpful. Furthermore, Group Therapy provides a group experience, which one may not be able to find elsewhere, that counteracts the emotionally pathological effects of the family group. It is recognized that a group feeling is essential in the development of all, and imperative in some, cases under treatment for emotional and mental disorders.

Chapter Eleven

RELATIONSHIP GROUP THERAPY WITH A MOTHER OF A PROBLEM CHILD*

Relationship Therapy, [1] as differentiated from other types of psychotherapy, is characterized by the fact that the therapist focuses his interpretation upon each patient's attitudes toward the therapist and toward the other members of the group. It bases itself on the principle that the patient will bring into the relationship with the therapist the emotions and patterns, both positive and negative, that he uses in his everyday contacts. The therapist becomes a target and buffer for all the personality patterns, workable or unworkable, that the patient uses with others. The therapeutic relation thus becomes a living experience in which the patient is able to release the whole gamut of feelings toward the therapist. The latter remains passive to the content of the patient's productions, but is active in pointing out the immediate underlying emotional drives. Immediate emotions are the feelings of which the patient is nearly aware and which he can face without too much anxiety.[2] The patient who is better integrated can absorb deeper interpretations sooner than one with more infantile personality, who is easily threatened.

* In this chapter, footnotes 5-25 are Dr. Pederson-Krag's comments.

[1] *Relationship Therapy* was first introduced by the late Dr. John Levy in 1938, and was carried on by some of his pupils since. See Levy, John: Relationship Therapy as Applied to Play Groups, *Am. J. Orthopsych.*, Oct., 1938; Durkin, Helen E., Glatzer, Henriette T., and Hirsch, Jeanette S.: Therapy of Mothers in Groups, *Am. J. Orthopsych.*, Jan., 1944; and Durkin, Helen E. and Glatzer, Henriette T.: The Role of the Therapist in Group Relationship Therapy, *Nerv. Child*, April, 1945; Durkin, Helen: John Levy's Relationship Therapy Applied to Play Groups, *Am. J. Orthopsych.*, July, 1939.

[2] On a once or twice a week basis, the therapist ought not let his patients grow too anxious.

The relationship therapist uses the relationship in two ways. He brings out those feelings of the patient that fall within the orbit of this new relationship and he points out substitutive functions of the therapist, interpreting the transference in the Freudian sense. In this way the patient becomes aware of his hitherto repressed feelings, re-lives some of his old conflicts and discovers how some of the neurotic defenses originated. The general aim is to help the patient to come to terms with himself. As in all other types of psychotherapy, here, too, the patient will choose what is appropriate for him and will modify his behavior and thinking when he comes to understand the interaction between his infantile drives and defenses, and his maladjustments. Not all patients need to reach the same depths in treatment or work through the same areas in order to make workable adjustments, and Relationship Therapy is, therefore, adjusted to the patient's immediate needs. Here the clinical judgment and experience of the therapist plays an essential part. The therapist must not only be able to judge when and how deep to carry the interpretations, but must be able to sense how much insight and transference catharsis is needed for each particular patient. The relationship therapist has to learn to evaluate and act upon the immediate needs in the treatment hour.

Observation of many mothers who brought their children for treatment showed that they needed help for themselves. It was found that making mothers aware of their own conflicts often served to help clear up their conflicts with their children. At the Brooklyn Child Guidance Center, where this work was initiated, the mothers, as well as the children, were treated in groups. From the very beginning the mothers' feelings were pointed out and clarified by the therapist as they emerged. Because their resistances and the transferences were dealt with directly, a group unity soon evolved, and the therapeutic process was stimulated. As the mothers found acceptance and understanding, they became more tolerant of themselves and of one another, and free to reveal and work through some of their deeper drives and defenses. As these feelings rose to the surface and were abreacted, the mothers grew receptive to interpretation and insight. As a result, their behavior patterns were modified, eliminated or controlled.

Groups have definite advantages aside from economy of time. The group highlights intra-familial transferences, stimulates inhibited patients to speak, encourages members during negative phases, and offers patients a unique opportunity to work out negative transferences on other group members, while retaining the positive transference toward the therapist.[3] Thus, the latter can be used as a valuable source of insight and emotional abreaction.

Mrs. Crimson, the mother whose therapeutic career will be described in the following case study was at first a member of a group of four Jewish women. As a rule we found it preferable to vary the religious, social and educational backgrounds of group members, because through this variety therapeutic elements in the group are stimulated.[4] However, in this group of women, the differences in the degree of religious observance served the same purpose.

Mrs. Crimson was referred to the guidance center by the principal of her son Kermit's school. She was a tall, attractive, neatly, but shabbily dressed woman with a mid-western accent. She was thirty-one years old and a graduate of business college. At the time of intake, she had a "nervous rash" on her hands. Mrs. Crimson appeared embarrassed and worried as she described Kermit's misbehavior. She seemed tense when she talked about the family's growing financial insecurity.

Mrs. Crimson asked for help for her nine year old son because of the many complaints from school and neighbors. Kermit was a school problem, did not get along well with his contemporaries, was over-aggressive and negativistic toward adults. He was jealous of his brother, Mickey, three-and-a-half years old, whom the parents described as a "perfect child." Kermit was irritable, given to crying spells, and had begun to bite his nails.

Mrs. Crimson reported that Kermit had been a problem since

[3] See Target Multiplicity, p. 37.

[4] Glatzer, Henriette T.: Selection of Mothers for Group Psychotherapy, *Amer. J. Orthopsych.*, July, 1947.

he was two-and-a-half years old and used to run away, occasionally, for four or five hours. His appetite had never been good. He always required special handling at school because of his "show off" behavior and his "so what" attitude. He was the object of ridicule by his classmates and played for attention. The family had moved many times and Kermit had been subjected to five changes in schools. The school sent for the mother frequently and Mrs. Crimson was embarrassed by it. Mr. Crimson said his wife "hounded" Kermit.

Mr. Crimson was a pleasant-faced, short man who was eleven years older than his wife. He worked at the seasonal trade of pattern-making and cutting. He had some facial tics, and gave the impression of being under tension; he spoke rapidly.

The psychiatric and psychological examinations showed that Kermit was a boy of average constitutional and intellectual development. His I. Q. was 107. It was obvious that Kermit was responding with aggressive behavior to his mother's emotional conflicts, and for this reason both mother and son needed treatment. Kermit was placed in a boys' group and Mrs. Crimson in a mothers' group.

When seen alone, Mrs. Crimson appeared hostile, suspicious and tense. She came late for the interview. She was helped to express her worry and uncertainty about taking this step. Apparently relieved by the therapist's sympathetic acceptance, Mrs. Crimson grew more communicative and freely expressed her bitterness about Kermit. She complained that he did not know how to play with children of his own age, bullied younger children, was a coward and seemed to hate her. [5]

Although she accepted verbally the idea of joining a mothers' group, she showed her resistance by objecting to the early hours of the group sessions and by expressing her doubt about the efficacy of play therapy for Kermit. This was the first time in the therapeutic situation that she used Kermit as a defense against

[5] This mother did not see she was rejecting her son; she was trying to persuade the therapist that her feelings toward him were entirely due to his antisocial behavior. This is typical of the reaction of a dependent person who blames the outer world for frustrating her inordinate demands.

facing a painful problem—the need to admit to herself that she was a patient. The therapist tried to help her recognize and express her fears about accepting treatment for herself, and also used this opportunity to prepare her for the length and discouraging aspects of treatment.

Since the focus is on Mrs. Crimson, the other three women in the group will be but briefly described. Mrs. Granite was another hostile, rejecting mother of a nine year old boy. She was at the "end of her rope" with him, and said she wanted help badly, yet she showed the same hostile reaction to treatment as she did to him. Her facial expression was sneering and supercilious. Mrs. Lilac, the third member, came because she was worried about the withdrawn, unsocial behavior of her nine year old son. She was an outgoing woman with unusual insight and, therefore, was very helpful to the group. Because of her frankness and less defensive manner, she played the part of a catalytic agent. She illustrates well the reason for trying to include less rigid, more insightful persons in every group.

Mrs. Olive, the fourth member, was a seriously disturbed, near-psychotic woman, who felt her nine year old daughter hated her, because the child disobeyed her. The other women had to be repeatedly protected from Mrs. Olive's remarks. The four women brought out their attitudes toward one another as well as toward the therapist. Mrs. Olive impeded group progress because her feelings were too intense and, therefore, created too much anxiety in the others. The first three women were put together because their sons' group met at the same time. Mrs. Olive was taken on as an experiment, since it was felt that the group experience might be beneficial to her.

Mrs. Crimson missed the first group session because Kermit was in the hospital, awaiting the decision as to whether or not he needed a mastoidectomy. At the second session, Mrs. Crimson described Kermit's illness. She was still waiting for the doctor's diagnosis. She expressed guilt over the uncontrollable rages she experienced, during which she beat him "dreadfully." She blamed herself for mishandling situations and wept as she described her visit to the hospital, where she could sense Kermit's resentment of her. Her anxiety and guilt were intensified by his serious illness and hospitalization to the extent that her unconscious hostility became a conscious emotional experience and could be recognized by her at the first interview. This was unusual, for ordinarily, mothers protested for months that they not only loved their children, but that they loved them too much. [6]

It was evident that Mrs. Crimson's hostility was close to the surface and had the effect of mobilizing the other women's hostility, so that they responded in kind, and many arguments were stirred up. [7]

Although it was a little early in treatment to highlight and reassure about strong contradictory feelings, this situation seemed to warrant it. Kermit's illness brought up Mrs. Crimson's fear of death. The therapist tried to generalize about loving and hating the same people, especially those with whom we are closely involved, and she illustrated with examples of infantile hostilities. Mrs. Crimson replied by telling how little Mickey shouted that he wished the doctor were dead when the latter injected him. When ambivalence was connected to death wishes, Mrs. Crimson exclaimed: "I'm so relieved, I thought it was monstrous to have such thoughts about the children." Mrs. Lilac continued with other illustrations of the same situation and stimulated the other two women to express their guilt and anxiety for having similar thoughts and wishes.

[6] This brings in a factor not typical of group or individual therapy—that of a dangerous situation in the outer world which makes the patient turn to actuality rather than indulge her unrealistic desires and defenses. This circumstance recalls shock therapy.

[7] This early interview illustrates how Group Therapy enhances catharsis. Had Mrs. Crimson told all this to a therapist in individual treatment, she might have assumed that his attitude toward her was one of benign tolerance. This would have considerably lessened her shame at revealing tendencies which she usually ignored. (An exception to this would have occurred if she had been exhibiting her failings for masochistic satisfaction.) However, in a group, Mrs. Crimson would rightly know that the other members' attitudes toward her were not those of a parent ideally kind and understanding, but those of society which is censorious. Thus, though she may well have said much less in a group than she would alone, her brief confession would afford her as much, if not more, relief of feelings than deeper material in individual therapy.

Mrs. Crismon was absent from the next two sessions because of Kermit's operation. At the fifth interview, the second for Mrs. Crimson, she came early. She was eager and friendly as she said she missed the group. The rapport she established at the first session indicated the beginning of a positive transference. This was evident in her defending treatment against the skepticism of Mrs. Granite and Mrs. Olive. She became the leader in revealing her guilt-laden relationship with Kermit. She felt ashamed of her inability to control her temper with Kermit while he was still convalescing. She seemed to gain insight into the causes of the family tensions as she voiced her feelings that she and her husband had been too strict with Kermit, and had been too partial to Mickey.

Mrs. Lilac, who had up to this time been silently critical of Mrs. Crimson and had been posing as extremely tolerant of her own children's behavior, began to respond to Mrs. Crimson's candor. She gradually related her resentment of her children, as she revealed that she sometimes felt like killing them all and making an end of it; perhaps they were born too soon after each other. Mrs. Crimson said with relief as Mrs. Lilac finished: "That's how I feel. I thought a mother must not feel like killing her children, and wanting to get rid of them. I feel so much better now that I hear the problems you mothers have. I could never even talk about my children to other people." [8]

At the following session, Mrs. Crimson, had gone back to her old defensive patterns. She parried with superficialities for a while

[8] Here one sees how a group can further the education of its members in a therapeutic manner more advantageously than can the individual worker. Every neurotic person has a distorted idea of reality that makes the expression of his drives easier. For instance, in this case, all the mothers professed ignorance that a mother-child relationship was not always entirely loving, whereas their experience of life must have shown them many cases when this was not so. However, because of their own fear of their hatred for their families, they were unaware of these. To maintain such a state of blindness required a psychic effort that resulted in tenseness, a characteristic often seen in mothers of problem children. When the other mothers learned this from Mrs. Crimson's frank revelation, they were less fearful of their own hostility, and could therefore face and eventually control it better. Whereas, if these members had been in individual therapy, their picture of normality represented by the therapist would have been largely made up of their own projected desires, ideals and idiosyncrasies.

and stressed good breeding, good table manners, truthfulness and impeccable behavior as worthy parental goals. From her tight-lipped expression and antagonistic remarks to Mrs. Lilac, it could be seen that she was growing resentful. When she could no longer control this resentment, she interrupted Mrs. Lilac to demand whether she or Mrs. Lilac handled their children correctly. Mrs. Lilac was over-indulgent to the point of indifference, while Mrs. Crimson was over-anxious and punitive. Mrs. Crimson's sibling rivalry was now close enough to the surface to be accessible to insight. In her request for the therapist's opinion, she was saying: "I am doing a better job than she; be on my side." Mrs. Olive at this time also became subject to this competition, and startled the women by demanding a division of time so no one woman could monopolize the hour, or waste time repeating herself. They were told that each one wanted the therapist's exclusive attention and resented sharing the hour. [9]

Toward the end of the hour, Mrs. Crimson began to wonder whether she had been overstressing the niceties of children's behavior. [10]

[9] We see here how the presence of other members intensified the transference reaction of each individual. Each patient was simultaneously confronted with a therapist who was a parent substitute, and a number of other patients with whom she had to share the therapist's attention. Sibling rivalry appeared. The advantages of this are obvious. In so far as group members had been plagued by the repression of this emotion they were able to feel relief as their sibling rivalry became manifest and could be demonstrated with impunity. On the other hand, sibling rivalry in individual therapy can only be discussed and elicited through persons not present, usually the therapist's other patients and friends. In the presence of sibling substitutes, each group member tries to make his bonds with the therapist firmer, either by silent identification, by accepting interpretations readily, by open competition with others, as in this session, and in other ways. Thus the dependent, demanding aspect of the transference is accentuated. Here was a therapeutic gain, for this type of relationship with the parents was a fertile cause of neurotic manifestations. On the other hand, in individual therapy, these transferences develop according to the pattern of the patient's unconscious strivings, and become apparent at the rate that his resistance allows.

[10] We note here that Mrs. Crimson's defenses against anxiety were crumbling under the impact of the others in the group. She had tried to hide her rejection of her children by holding up an ideal of courtesy; she realized the flimsiness of this defense when it was not endorsed by the therapist and by the group members.

Mrs. Olive proved to be a disturbing group member. She either plunged into repressed conflicts too soon or diverted the other women from approaching deeper feelings. For instance, when the other women discussed the embarrassing behavior of their children, Mrs. Olive described how her dog had embarrassed her by soiling the carpet of a friend. When Mrs. Crimson summoned enough courage to describe her intimacy with her father, Mrs. Olive criticized her severely and then began to weep copiously as she mentioned her own family. Once at the beginning of an hour, she arose to say that since she did not care about the personal problems of the other women, she was going downstairs to talk to the office secretary.

At the eighth interview, the other women discussed Mrs. Olive resentfully before she arrived. Their hostility was brought out and related to treatment. The therapist's acceptance and tolerance of hostility was instrumental in helping Mrs. Lilac reveal her uneasiness about her daughter's jealousy of her for her husband's affection. This shocked Mrs. Crimson who could not bear to face this painful material and she regressed to her customary defense, Kermit's difficulties, this time blaming the school. As sympathetically as possible, the therapist pointed this out.

At the ninth interview, with some of the sibling tensions cleared at the last session, Mrs. Crimson's need to fight with Mrs. Lilac had decreased. She let Mrs. Lilac recount her girlhood experiences without interrupting. Mrs. Lilac revealed that she had a tyrannical father and was in constant fear of him. Since Mrs. Crimson's resistance had been broken through she could respond to Mrs. Lilac's confidences.[11]

When Mrs. Lilac finished speaking, Mrs. Crimson recalled her wonderful father and contrasted him with her strict, stern mother. Her mother died when she was thirteen years old, after a long illness during which Mrs. Crimson had little contact with her. Mrs. Crimson said that after a choleric scene with the children she hated herself for acting toward them as her mother had toward her. She was afraid that her children would feel toward

---

[11] Such a member not only educates the others, but also helps them to produce cathartic material, as they compete with each other.

her as she had felt toward her mother. She despairingly repeated the unbridled language she used and expressed the fear that she would get a stroke and die. Thus Mrs. Crimson identified with her mother in her hostility to the children, and saw that she did to them what her mother had done to her. Her guilt about this attitude expressed itself in recurrent depressions.

It was at the tenth interview that a discussion of religious customs took place. Mrs. Crimson and Mrs. Granite disagreed with Mrs. Lilac who expressed her disdain for religion. When the therapist connected religious attitudes with family attitudes, Mrs. Lilac said she associated religion with her hated father, who was orthodox. Mrs. Crimson boasted about the beautiful religious atmosphere her father had created in their home. She idealized the close relationship she had with her father for five years after her mother's death. She gave up friends in order to be his constant companion. The early death of her mother and her father's indulgence and sympathy intensified the oepidal relation and brought it close to the surface and, therefore, made it accessible to early treatment. She described her step-mother in resentful terms and tearfully recounted how her father was weaned from herself. The rivalry with her step-mother was a constant source of irritation and after four unhappy years, she left for New York to find a job and to live with her rich married sister. [12]

At the end of this session, Mrs. Crimson's resistance to treatment came out in her complaints about revealing so much of her personal life. The resistance really was against revealing resentment of her husband. More direct criticisms of him had been appearing and she was becoming increasingly aware of them.

Having broken through her resistance in the previous session, she could give vent to her pent-up sibling hostility directly in this session. She argued with the other women first, and then poured out her resentment of her children and even began to complain

[12] We are now beginning to get an inkling of why Mrs. Crimson was so persistently hostile. We have noted that she was a demanding, dependent woman which would give her the impression, possibly justified, that her mother was a cold, rejecting person from whom she could never get enough. In addition, she had been disappointed in her father when he remarried, as the therapist pointed out to her. Her disappointment in her parents was carried over to her children.

about her husband. She said that Mickey's behavior made her so nervous that she felt like a crazy woman. The skin on her hands had broken out again and she had not been able to sleep. She was humiliated by the neighbors' constant complaints about Mickey and was ashamed that she had begun to beat the children in the street. Whenever her resistance was worked out, she could admit that Mickey was a problem. This meant that she could admit that family relationships were involved, since she could not use her defense of blaming the school for Mickey's failings. Mrs. Crimson could now recognize that she "took out her nervousness" on Kermit "who was lovely and considerate" throughout this episode. She began to cry and expressed surprise since she rarely gave way to tears. She sank back into her chair, spent with emotion. Toward the end of the session she revealed she would like to go back to work where she had been successful, but she felt too guilty toward the children.

Her conflict over her feminine role was emerging but it was considered that this problem was not too closely related to her complaints and, therefore, it was not necessary to work through that area to help her achieve the necessary emotional readjustment. The therapist emphasized instead her guilty relationship to her children by saying that sometimes mothers made exaggerated sacrifices to make up for not loving their children as much as they felt they should. Mrs. Crimson began to understand the connection between her over-conscientious attitude and her guilt feelings toward her children; she admitted that she wanted to send them to summer camp, but felt too guilty to allow herself that freedom.

Mrs. Crimson had a half hour alone at the twelfth session because the other women were late or absent. She expressed discouragement with her family and wished she could walk out on them. Her husband was out of work and she left him home frequently to visit with her wealthy girl friend. She criticized her friend's dejection for being barren, and wished she were "in her shoes." Her dissatisfaction with her meek, short, acquiescent husband rose closer to surface as she discussed disappointment in marriages and gave a few examples. The therapist related her disappointment in marriage to her father's second marriage. Although she denied any connection, she immediately gave an account of her unwilling marriage to her husband. Mrs. Crimson fell madly in love with her husband's tall, handsome brother. When she found that he merely wanted an affair with her, she felt hurt and chagrined and agreed to marry his brother, her present husband, but only after he promised to release her if he could not make her happy. Soon after the marriage, her husband lost his money and she became the only one of her sisters who had to "pinch pennies." She dreaded visiting home to be received as the poor relative. She confided to the group that if her husband were not good and understanding, she would have left him.[13]

At the following session, Mrs. Crimson told the group how much she got "off her chest" last week, how relieved she felt and what a good week she had. This boasting was an outcome of her sibling rivalry and offered her the opportunity to flaunt that she had had the therapist all to herself. She drained off hostility to the children at this interview too, but felt less guilty. She became quite tense as she criticized Mrs. Lilac's easy attitude toward money, but when the therapist explained how envy was often disguised by critical attitudes, she soon admitted her envy of Mrs. Lilac's financial security.

At the fourteenth session, we find Mrs. Crimson more ambivalent and less constantly hostile to her children, for the rivalry was being acted out in the group instead.[14]

Mrs. Crimson spent the last five minutes of the hour describing in glowing terms her duties as a nurses' aid. Her expression relaxed as she recounted her happiness in doing constructive work. She now felt that she could assume an important role

[13] This was for the most part an individual interview. We see how Mrs. Crimson makes use of it to confide intimate details to the therapist, as though holding her tighter with a secret. This also illustrates her strong exhibitionistic tendencies which had already been very evident in her leadership in giving material.

[14] Mrs. Crimson's conduct in the sessions suggest what her childhood was like; there was a kind father for whose attention a number of children competed. Sometimes they competed by being particularly smart—as she had done on occasion—sometimes by being sick and demanding sympathy as she had done for her troubles.

should disaster strike (during the war) and that she would be able to support herself and the children should anything happen to her husband.[15]

At the last interview before summer vacation, the fifteenth, Mrs. Crimson said that she felt considerably calmed. She no longer felt the need to watch the children so carefully and as a result did not become as irritable. She was happy about Kermit's improvement in school. Mrs. Crimson's outside activities kept her too busy to worry about her sons and she had arranged to send them to summer camp.

In summarizing the treatment up to this point, we see that Mrs. Crimson's need to drain off long pent-up hostility and to gain attention was relieved in the permissive atmosphere of the group, with an accepting mother figure. She expressed hostility directly against the children and reactivated her sibling jealousies on the other group members. As her sibling jealousies were diverted, they decreased toward her sons. She had less anxiety after she recognized her ambivalent feelings to her father and husband, and consequently hostility meant for them was not as frequently displaced on Kermit. Mrs. Crimson grew less guilty toward the children and could even send them to camp. She externalized some of her hostility and guilt and therefore replaced destructive patterns with constructive ones. She could now use her energies effectively and she took up outside interests. As a result of lifting the first layers of anxiety in treatment, she was temporarily happier and less tense.

The composition of the group changed somewhat after the summer vacation. Mrs. Olive was replaced by Mrs. Beige, a Protestant woman. Mrs. Beige had been treated individually at a child guidance clinic in another city and it was felt she could adjust to this group without too much difficulty. She was essentially a cold, neurotic, dependent, over-anxious woman whose

[15] It is interesting to note that she is anticipating rather favorably, disaster either on a wide scale or to her husband. This suggests that her hostility is still present though now concealed.

relationship with her nine year old son was tense. The child was hyper-active, infantile and had difficulties at school.

At the first interview after vacation, Mrs. Crimson came twenty minutes late. She seemed restrained by the new member and probably also because of the summer interval. Kermit's remarkable improvement in school and her ability to control herself made her wonder whether Kermit ought to continue in treatment. She was afraid he would get into bad habits again through the group. The therapist pointed out her resistance and related it to the usual resentment of treatment after vacation. All the women voiced their agreement and discussed these matters.[16]

At the seventeenth session, Mrs. Crimson again came late and when this was called to her attention as resistance, she said that she was "all mixed up." She had resumed slapping the children and no longer could control her temper. She expressed her guilt and mentioned several times that she had something on her mind, but gave no details. The therapist said that perhaps she was troubled about something, but she refrained from talking about it probably because of the new member, Mrs. Beige.

At the next two sessions, Mrs. Crimson was afforded little opportunity to say much, since Mrs. Beige dominated the conversation. She was merely able to tell, with little or no effect, about beating Kermit for his abusive language.

At the following interview Mrs. Crimson said that she felt frustrated by Kermit. She had been beating him again and disclosed her hatred of him. She suffered from dizzy spells after each beating. Her hostility to her husband was evident in her description of the tongue lashing she gave him when he wanted to discipline Kermit for her. She was again using Kermit as an outlet for her anxiety. The anxiety, in turn, was a defense against voicing hostility to her husband. The therapist picked up the thread about her husband and indicated her reluctance to discuss him in front of the new member. Mrs. Crimson agreed and voiced her discouragement with the treatment. These doubts were

---

[16] Here resistance is expressed, as it often is in individual treatment, by declaring that the original symptoms for which therapy was sought have diminished.

linked with her resistance by the therapist. This opened the flood-gates, as it were. In an agitated voice, Mrs. Crimson recalled her quarrel with her husband that morning. When she asked him for additional luxuries, he suggested that she go to work. Mrs. Crimson berated him angrily and declared that she did not want to work to supplement his small income. She wanted to have sufficient money, like her older sisters, without working for it.

At the twenty-second interview, Mrs. Crimson expressed her envy of Mrs. Granite's private session with the therapist, who pointed out that Mrs. Crimson found it as difficult to share this parent-figure as it had been to share her father with her sisters. A little later Mrs. Crimson became furious when Mrs. Granite described her son's misbehavior. She shouted: "I don't know why I come to a Guidance Centre. I don't get any guidance. Why don't you tell me how to handle Kermit? He's driving me crazy. It can't go on. What good are you doing?" She asked for advice and when it was not forthcoming screamed that she would throw her bag at the therapist. It was explained to her that she was acting out her hostility to the bad parent who favored her sister. A little later she stated how she had assailed Kermit when he refused to eat all of his sandwich at lunch. She recognized that her rage was disproportionate and wondered why she could not ignore his eating habits. The therapist related her need to make him eat with her guilt feelings toward him.

Mrs. Crimson then confessed that she did not like children, did not want them around, never played with her boys because they bored her, and hated to be home with them. She asked the therapist's advice as to whether she ought to go to work or stay home. She had made all arrangements to enter the children at a private all-day school, but felt uneasy about leaving them. She realized as she talked, that she really did not want to work, but felt there was no other way of getting away from her sons.[17]

---

[17] This was a very useful session therapeutically. Mrs. Crimson was angry, both with Mrs. Granite and the therapist, because of Mrs. Granite's private interview. As she could express her fury in a limited way only by threatening, she turned to tell of her attacking her son, substituting him for the therapist. It is understandable why in the next interview she was much calmer and relieved.

Mrs. Crimson arrived at the following interview in a tranquil mood, feeling encouraged by Kermit's behavior and her ability to handle the family problems easily. At the twenty-fourth session, there was a growing recognition of her resentment and jealousy of her rich older sister. At the following session, Mrs. Crimson came in demanding advice about controlling Kermit who had become a "hellion" five days ago. It was evident by her hostile, demanding attitude that she was deeply stirred up. When the therapist commented on her being worried, she denied it, but soon told of her out-of-town sister's visit. Her feelings of insecurity were reactivated by her sister's critical attitude. She described with considerable tension that nothing she did or had done pleased her sister, who told her frankly that she preferred to stay with the other sister. She felt she could never win her sisters' love.

From this interview on, Mrs. Crimson became aware of her identification of her unfriendly sisters with her mother. She felt highly sensitive to their rejection which reminded her of her mother's unloving attitude to her. She came to realize how her futile efforts to placate and win them over merely increased her sense of inadequacy, how she tormented herself and her family in her attempts to live up to their expectations and how all their visits deepened her rage and depression.[18]

Ever since treatment had begun, there was evidence that Mrs. Crimson unconsciously identified Mrs. Lilac with her father, because Mrs. Lilac was apparently easygoing and taunted the other women by the ease with which she handled her children. The therapist pointed out that talking about fathers directly was painful to Mrs. Crimson. This became apparent when Mrs. Lilac described how her father had been unfaithful to his wife and had neglected herself and the other children.

At the twenty-sixth interview, this came to a head. Mrs. Crimson and Mrs. Granite walked in a little late, conversing. Instead of listening to what the other women were saying, Mrs. Crimson

[18] This was a repetition of her early trauma resulting from her siblings having been preferred.

interrupted them to continue her tirade against Kermit. She was furious with him for failing his arithmetic examination. Her voice grew louder, surlier and more hostile. Mrs. Lilac, who was angry with Mrs. Crimson for interrupting her, burst forth that she would not want Mrs. Crimson for a mother and if she were Kermit, she would behave even worse. Mrs. Lilac's past descriptions of her childhood behavior toward her father seemed to parallel Kermit's. Mrs. Crimson defended her attitude. and shouted that she had been brought up to be respectful and Kermit would either be killed or learn to respect her. Mrs. Lilac said no child could respect such a mother. She added that Mrs. Crimson was dissatisfied with her husband and their economic insecurity and took it out on Kermit. Mrs. Crimson became enraged and called Mrs. Lilac so "wishy-washy" that she could not command respect from her children. Mrs. Granite sided with Mrs. Crimson.

The epithets these women used about each other were almost identical to those used in their earlier descriptions of their fathers. The therapist stepped in to say that their feelings were not meant for each other personally, that Mrs. Lilac saw in Mrs. Crimson her stern father and Mrs. Crimson saw in Mrs. Lilac her easygoing father who suddenly turned against her. Mrs. Lilac said: "That's so, she's just like him, a tyrant." Mrs. Crimson seemed surprised and then said slowly: "And she is as easygoing as he was; he threw me out, yes he did . . . I really want to have Mrs. Lilac's easygoing nature, but I also want to command respect." Her anger against Mrs. Lilac was gone. She began to reflect about her attitude toward Kermit. This time when she said she was at fault, it seemed that the newly gained insight was more integrated into her personality. The therapist tried to help her by saying that she must have wondered why her rage against Kermit was uncontrollable, and emphasized that children's behavior often unleashed parents' pent-up feelings. Mrs. Beige, moved by the confessions of the two women began to analyze her relationship to her father. Mrs. Crimson interrupted Mrs. Beige to tell Mrs. Granite something inconsequential. The therapist called to Mrs. Crimson's notice that she still seemed to find it uncomfortable to listen to father-daughter relationships.[19]

When time was up, Mrs. Crimson threatened to bang the therapist over the head with her shoe, if the hour again were ended before she had completed recounting everything she had to say.

At the twenty-seventh interview, Mrs. Crimson was able to connect Kermit's becoming a problem with her husband's slack work-seasons. She seemed to understand it for the first time. She turned to Mrs. Granite and attacked her for not revealing anything personal and for not having any real trouble because her husband also had a steady income. She expressed annoyance because she found that she, and not Kermit, was the problem. She became red in the face as she demanded from the therapist: "Well, what about you? We know you are married; have you any children? How do they behave?" The therapist responded to this, by telling her that this knowledge would not help her with her own problems and that this attack was a way of avoiding a further discussion of painful feelings, since this had been pointed out many times. before and Mrs. Crimson was aware of her defense. She now was ready for an interpretation of her transference feelings so it was stressed that she felt as angry against the therapist as she had against her father and she was also reassured that getting angry was a part of the treatment. The identification of the therapist with the father had been anticipated in her threat to the therapist at the end of the previous session. The type of attack was more like that directed against Mrs. Lilac and less like her former demands on the therapist.

At the next four sessions, there were abrupt changes in mood. Mrs. Crimson appeared at the twenty-eighth session feeling happy about Kermit's good marks. The next time she arrived late—tense and discouraged about a fight she had with neighbors. At the following meeting she came in with only nice things to

[19] This was a climactic session. Not only was sibling rivalry revealed, but also the cross-identification of group members with each other's fathers. Here the superficial sibling rivalry was less important than the deeper oedipal disappointment felt by both women.

relate about Kermit. She began to recognize her compulsive drive to keep the house clean and tidy. Since this anal material was not too closely related to her present problems, it did not seem necessary to work through it to help her make an adequate readjustment. Her resentment of her children for interfering with her routine only were, therefore, emphasized. She could accept this and seemed to gain more insight into her rivalry relationship with her children.

Mrs. Crimson seemed defensive and irritable at the thirty-second session. She became aroused by Mrs. Lilac's casual attitude toward a school complaint. When Mrs. Lilac recounted dancing with a Chinese at a social function, the other three women shuddered, but it was only Mrs. Crimson who attacked Mrs. Lilac. She said: "You do everything for a good time. You pose as being a liberal, but you only do it to get a thrill. You like drinking." Mrs. Lilac retorted: "I don't dance with everyone. I was pleased this man selected me, he was an educated gentleman. Anyway, you envy me because you can't enjoy yourself and you can't drink." Mrs. Crimson replied: "I drink too, but I don't like the way you brag." [20]

The therapist explained to Mrs. Crimson that people often criticized what they wanted and then told Mrs. Lilac that she liked to tease Mrs. Crimson by over-emphasizing whatever she thought Mrs. Crimson did not like, and pointed up her indirect way of attacking people. When Mrs. Crimson said she envied Mrs. Lilac's financial security, Mrs. Lilac offered to give up her husband to Mrs. Crimson. Mrs. Crimson replied: "I don't need him. Mine is grand, too grand, too good; that's the trouble!" She was then stimulated to express her full resentment of her "kind, considerate husband." When the other women envied her, Mrs. Crimson dismissed this by wishing for financial security. It can be seen that money meant love to Mrs. Crimson. Financial security was a defense against any sudden withdrawal of love as

[20] Here the group situation recalled what happened when Mrs. Crimson's sister visited New York. Though Mrs. Crimson's hostile feelings had decreased, they welled up on slight provocation against Mrs. Lilac, upon whom she had a transference that was derived partly from her feelings to her father and partly from those to her siblings.

experienced by her father's abrupt remarriage. Money seemed to represent reassurance of always being loved.[21]

At the next eight interviews, Mrs. Crimson was able to disclose her displeasure with her husband for not being more virile. As a significant result of her and Mrs. Lilac's having both worked out rivalry and hostility, Mrs. Lilac dropped her defensive attitude and revealed her worry about her husband's sanity, and Mrs. Crimson began to sympathize with Mrs. Lilac. Mrs. Crimson could now take good-naturedly Mrs. Lilac's criticism of her as a "nag" and a "shrew" and even saw justification for those terms. Mrs. Crimson seemed to be getting along well with her family.

At the forty-first interview, Mrs. Crimson appeared disturbed and told of Kermit's becoming hateful again. The therapist indicated to Mrs. Crimson that this was the usual resistance before giving painful material. She then revealed her apprehension concerning her sister's forthcoming visit. The therapist connected her tenseness with anticipating fear of being rejected by a mother-figure. During the same session Mrs. Crimson disclosed that the characteristics she disliked most in Kermit were his conceit and selfishness, the very same characteristics she resented in her brother-in-law. When this was called to her attention, she admitted that Kermit looked like him. The therapist said that Kermit probably received a lot of feelings meant for her brother-in-law, and sympathized with her for having a child who reminded her of an ex-suitor who had rejected her; old hurts were not easily forgotten. Her response expressed her gain in emotional maturity: "I have been using Kermit as a punching bag for all my feelings. I think I needed treatment more than he did."

At the next series of interviews, Mrs. Crimson became more cognizant of her feelings of rivalry with Kermit. She could now understand that she refused him pets because she had wanted to get even with him. It became obvious to her that she resented sharing her home and furniture with the children. She was happy in being recognized and praised by people she admired in the

---

[21] Mrs. Crimson's predominantly oral character had been revealed at the beginning of therapy. Here we see evidence of it again: what her husband gives her is not enough.

PTA and war organizations. She had organized a first-aid crew on her block which had been extolled for its efficiency. Having worked through a good deal of sibling rivalry, she was able to get along with siblings in general. She now felt free enough to send the children to camp.

There were discussions on sex, during which both Mrs. Crimson and Mrs. Granite decided that all men were over-demanding and Mrs. Crimson revealed that she was mostly cold to her "over-demanding" husband. She could now divulge that her attractive, tall brother-in-law had always had strong physical appeal to her. She not only could face that her husband was the opposite of her father and brother-in-law, but could accept him better for his own qualities.[22]

At the last interview, the forty-sixth, Mrs. Crimson described her quarrels with her sister who was visiting her at the time. She tried to mollify this wealthy sister by giving her gifts, but when she did not succeed, she expressed her feelings toward her sister directly. She became aware that her irritability with Kermit at this time was due to her jealousy of Kermit because he was preferred by this sister. She recognized that their getting together reminded her of her childhood when her siblings ganged up on her. She was pleased that she could control her feelings toward the boy and was relieved that she could tell her sister how she really felt. Her efforts to win over her sisters who represented her mother, and her strong need to find a good mother, were discussed in this session. She recalled her spells of weeping as a child because she did not have the same kind mother that her friends had. Mrs. Crimson could understand the conflict between her dependent need to have her husband baby her, and her resentment of his not being much of a man when he did.

Mrs. Crimson went through many emotional crises in treatment and at home. During these periods she used Kermit as the "whipping boy." Gradually she became aware that she not only

[22] Here her life history had repeated itself. She had been frustrated by her father's marrying again, and by her brother-in-law, who resembled him, marrying another woman after jilting her.

used him in that way at home, but utilized talking of her anger against him as resistance to revealing her hidden feelings. After this had been broken through repeatedly, she gained enough insight to modify her need to use Kermit as the victim of her resentments. The group situation gave her the opportunity to work out her sibling rivalry with the group members. As this rivalry was reactivated and dispelled in the group, less was displaced on Kermit, with the attendant improvement in his relationship with her. After the sibling jealousies had been handled in the group, Mrs. Crimson became able to drain off her resentment of her father through the person of Mrs. Lilac. The hostility resulting from being rejected by her father had been displaced onto the brother-in-law who also did not want her, and thence to Kermit. When Mrs. Crimson grew aware of this, another reason for releasing hostility upon Kermit was diminished. Toward the end of treatment, as a result of "working through" sibling rivalry, Mrs. Crimson was able to get along with her contemporaries in clubs, patriotic organizations, schools, and the like. She realized that she had been treating the other members and, therefore, people in general as though they were her critical sisters who never could be placated. This insight enabled her to be less expectant of criticism and friendly with persons she encountered. She even became sympathetic to the previously much disliked group member, Mrs. Lilac. Mrs. Crimson was now praised for her abilities by people she admired.[23]

In the transference relationship, the therapist was often used as a hostile, rejecting parent, and sometimes as an ideal parent. With hostility lessened, Mrs. Crimson was able to resolve resentment of her husband for not being virile like her tall father. Financial security was recognized as a need to be loved. Resentment of her husband for his inability to provide was eased. Mrs. Crimson was able to help him with their financial burdens.

She returned a year later to tell us that she was running a boarding house in the country and was enjoying the experience.

[23] At this point, real gratification came to the therapist's aid in giving Mrs. Crimson less reason for feeling inadequate and rejected.

She sold all the furniture which had caused so much friction between her and the children and was thinking of buying a hotel at some winter resort. She said she felt like a new woman. The children were little trouble to her and she laughed at her former inability to cope with them.[24]

Kermit had achieved a fine record in school and did get along well with other children, and with his brother. His general adjustment was satisfactory.[25]

[24] All this indicates a drastic lessening of hostility and ensuing guilt and anxiety that had previously hampered her relations with outsiders and with her own family. True, she was still frigid, and had some masculine identifications, but these were not enough to warrant further therapy.

[25] No special mention has been made of the psychodynamics of the other members, but they, too, were able to benefit by Mrs. Crimson's outpourings. This contrasts with individual therapy where silence or frivolous and irrelevant remarks indicate that the patient is unable to expose his deeper emotions and conflicts. In Group Therapy this is not necessarily so. A group member who says little for several meetings may well be sharing vicariously in the sentiments and experiences described by others. Thus he obtains some slight catharsis and understanding of his own psyche. His resistance, if strong, would be likely to appear by absenting himself from subsequent meetings or by contradicting what has been said by others. In other cases, he observes that the habits he had thought inevitable and fully justified are less worthy of continuing than those displayed by other members of the group. This strengthens the patient's ability to make better adjustments than before.

Chapter Twelve

DIDACTIC GROUP PSYCHOTHERAPY WITH PSYCHOTIC PATIENTS

The problem of the definition of a psychosis is well-nigh insoluble. It is not enough to say that a psychosis is a mental illness, because such a statement requires one to define what mental illness is. Only the uninitiated could dare offer a definition, but this would inevitably include the stigma and horror that for centuries were invested in the concept of mental disorders. One can say with a reasonable degree of assurance that the psychotic is mentally more sick than most other people. The particular quality of his illness, as far as it can be identified, is the fact that the psychotic patient, as a result of his internal conflicts has, by and large, abandoned the principle of reality as a guiding principle in his adjustment to the outside world.

This definition implies a diagnostic criterion far more sharply delineated than is actually the case. The psychotic is not incapable of distinguishing reality from fantasy. He *is* able to distinguish them, but it does not greatly matter to him which is which. Every patient, who is not in a state of far advanced deterioration can invariably distinguish between the real and the unreal when properly treated and encouraged. He *can* distinguish the difference, but the difficulty is, that to him the difference is unimportant. He can, therefore, employ reality and fantasy interchangeably. In most instances, the patient's psychotic state lies not in the fact that he cannot recognize what is reality and what is fantasy, but to him the distinction is of no consequence. His disease is, therefore, in a sense, indifference.

The foregoing would indicate that a psychosis is not a matter of quality, but of quantity, and that no sharp line of demarcation can be drawn between so-called normality and mental illness. It should also help to underscore the fact that though we are dealing with individuals whom the law has labelled "insane," no hard and fast rules can be drawn about what is and what is not practicable in the realm of the psychoses.

This chapter is necessarily limited to Group Therapy in mental institutions, because Group Therapy with private patients is only in its beginning stages and has been tried by only a few psychiatrists. Among these are A. A. Low of Chicago, and this writer. As a matter of fact, it was found that the very practice of Group Therapy itself results in the formation of some sort of an institution, using the term in a somewhat broader sense than is that of "mental hospital." However, the distinction is of very little importance and group practices, whether employed in a large mental hospital or with private patients, tend to be the same and governed by the same principles.

The traditional form of treatment of psychotic patients has been social sequestration in institutions formerly known as "insane asylums," but in modern times hopefully renamed "mental hospitals." Sequestration of psychotics is still regarded as the aim of hospitalization by many. Expanding knowledge of the dynamics of adjustment, however, plainly indicates that the real aim of hospital treatment should be reintegration of the patient into society, and many hospitals are making strides in that direction, though lack of public support, of trained personnel and of other facilities make the progress rather slow. The newer methods of treatment, such as the shock therapies, are not proving to be panaceas, and it is universally conceded that even they do not yield optimum benefits, unless accompanied by collateral psychotherapy. It may be that there is considerable variance of opinion among psychiatrists as to the future role of the mental hospital, but a keynote has been struck by Marsh [1] who has stated:

"Institutions for mental patients should be considered 'schools' rather than hospitals. The author's experiment has demonstrated that mental patients can be instructed in groups.and thus receive

[1] Marsh, L. C.: Group Treatment of the Psychoses by the Psychological Equivalent of Revival. *Ment. Hyg.*, April, 1931.

the re-education that we have talked about . . . The mental patient should be regarded not as a patient, but as a student who has received a 'condition' in the great subject of civilization, as most of us understand it, and psychiatry should thus approach him with an intent to re-educate rather than with an attempt to 'treat'."

Group psychotherapy would seem to be an ideal procedure to carry out Marsh's vision of a mental hospital.

Experience so far tends to indicate that there is some reciprocal relationship between individual and group psychotherapy in the treatment of psychotics. They appear to complement each other. Patients with whom a positive transference can be established only after months of individual treatment, if at all, may be able to overcome their resistance under the influence of a group and make a working relationship with the therapist possible, sometimes after only a few "class" sessions. Many patients approach the therapist of their own accord after a class session and ask for a personal interview. This alone would justify the conclusion that, at the very least, group psychotherapy is an effective preparation for individual psychotherapy with psychotics.

Sherman [2] seems to have arrived at much the same conclusion when he states: "There seems to be a general agreement that individual psychoanalytic procedures do not fulfill all the therapeutic needs of the patient. All those problems and conflicts which come roughly within the domain of the social superego do not seem to get properly worked out. The patient, returned to society, may find that his relationship with people at large is still grossly distorted . . ."

It is quite probable that group treatment is more effective in certain areas that have remained relatively untouched by individual treatment. It seems reasonable that correction of deficiencies in social attitudes is best accomplished in a social setting. In any case, the rapidity with which a positive working relationship is formed with the patient in group psychotherapy, which is often

[2] Sherman, S.: A System of Combined Individual and Group Therapy as Used in the Medical Program for Merchant Seamen. *Amer. J. Psychiat.*, July, 1943.

carried over to individual interviews, indicates its strong catalytic action.

Group psychotherapy in hospitals appears to have had its origin as an expedient to economize time and to enable the psychiatrists to treat more patients. As it sometimes happens, the expedient was found to have virtues in its own right. However, it does not displace individual therapy and, when at all possible, should be administered in conjunction with it. Thus instead of saving it appears to necessitate a greater expenditure of time. But despite the fact that patients are seen in groups or classes, as well as individually, the advantage is still on the side of group psychotherapy. Because of the catalytic action of the group sessions, it may be sufficient to see each patient for not more than fifteen to twenty minutes once a week, and perhaps even less, instead of the usual hour sessions two or three times weekly.

". . . Group and individual psychotherapies are not antagonists or competitors. They are collaborators and complement each other. While the most intensive results in affective reorientation are probably best achieved in individual psychotherapy, such as psychoanalysis, the optimum results in reorientative psychotherapy are likely best achieved in group treatment. For reorientation to the world of reality is invariably in terms of the social milieu, and just as the patient experiences the most intimate affect through the person of a significant parent-surrogate in the transference, in the same way it is logical to believe his social relationships are best re-experienced in relation to the group." [3]

The general psychodynamics of Group Therapy are applicable with all groups and these have been delineated elsewhere in this book. (See Chapter I).

There are, however, some special aspects of psychodynamics as they apply to groups or classes of psychotic patients. The word "class" is here used in its purely academic sense, that is, a group of patients who voluntarily report at stated periods to receive the ministrations of the group therapist.

[3] Klapman, J. W.: *Group Psychotherapy, Theory and Practice*, New York, Grune & Stratton, 1946, pp. 119-120.

There are patients who are in a state of acute psychosis so intense that it would appear at first that little can be gained for them through "class" instruction. But this is precisely one of the most important values of group psychotherapy with psychotics as compared with individual treatment. The problem of the extent of a patient's disturbance that will nevertheless permit his inclusion in the class without too great a hindrance to the others remains still to be determined. Disturbed and more or less acutely psychotic patients brought to class often become so absorbed that after several sessions they become active participants in the group, with resulting improvement. The example set by the therapist and the relatively unconflicted patients has a therapeutic effect and helps to bring the new member into the current of the group formation. This mechanism has been demonstrated in experimentation with animals. Masserman [4] reports that a "conflicted" cat, who was afraid to approach the feeding box when alone, was gradually able to make tentative attempts to take food through observing the normal cat eating from the box. This type of behavior was adopted by a paranoid patient who observed a group in action. A therapy group met on the ward where in the mornings he and other patients received insulin hypoglycemic shock treatment. In the afternoons, Vernon would lie fully clothed on his bed, about twenty-five feet from where the group was assembled, holding recitations and discussions. Loudly swearing and showering threats and vituperations upon the therapist and various patients in the class, Vernon attempted to disrupt the proceedings. After several weeks of this he still would pick up some statement made in class and guffaw over it. Gradually, from his perch he truculently began to ask questions, which no one answered. Occasionally he would attempt to answer a question addressed to someone else in the class. Finally, after a number of weeks he joined the class voluntarily and took part in the classwork in a co-operative and friendly manner. Before he was released he had become a reasonable and agreeable individual, taking a very intelligent interest in the work of

[4] Masserman, J.: *Behavior and Neurosis*, Chicago, Univ. of Chicago Press, 1943.

the class. We do not know whether he was "cured," but at the time of his release he was enjoying at least an excellent remission.

The various psychodynamics of the personality that are modified by the group in psychotic patients can be described as follows:

(a) *Patient-to-Patient Transferences.* We have already seen that in such groups a transference toward the therapist exists, and as an indirect result also patient-to-patient transferences appear. The latter go beyond the hospital classroom, for the patient-to-patient transferences tend to carry over into the post-hospitalization period. This accounts for the several ex-patients' organizations now functioning in various parts of the country. The patients' organization in itself is a therapeutic agent, and it is no mere accident that such an organization as Alcoholics Anonymous has assumed national proportions. The patients' organizations help to provide a transition through which patients are shielded against the shock of suddenly facing the pressures of society. Ex-patients provide ego-support to each other. With the help of such an association many patients may remain useful members of society for indefinite periods, whereas otherwise intermittent periods of hospitalization may be necessary. Federn [5] has recommended that a psychotic patient should always have a person in the post-hospitalization period to whom he may relate himself in a positive transference. Without such assistance improvement is bound to be, in most instances, only temporary.

The value of a treatment procedure in mental disorders cannot always be judged by complete "cures" effected by it. It frequently has to be employed as an accessory and not an absolute cure. It must be recognized that there is a point in mental disorders beyond which the pathology is no longer reversible, and their parallelism with cardiac valvular disorders, for example, will make this clear. The objective of the cardiologist in such cases is not "cure," but keeping the patient compensated and as comfortable as possible. This is considered a worthwhile achievement, although, patently, the patient will continue to need medical

[5] Federn, P.: Psychoanalysis of Psychoses. *Psychiat. Quart.*, January, April, July, 1943.

attention and supervision for the rest of his life. This is equally true of some psychotic patients. They need prolonged extramural supervision in the post-hospitalization period while they make their way back into society, and even after. Organized groups for ex-patients can do much to supply them with the much needed ego-support.

(b) *Catharsis.* In large mental institutions most of the work with patients is of a routine nature. A number of institutions, especially of the private and smaller type, are able to arrange for more or less frequent private interviews with psychiatrists. In the large state hospital, however, there is hardly a better therapeutic means to be found than Group Psychotherapy sessions. The therapeutic atmosphere created in the group and remarks made by patients and psychiatrist, stimulate catharsis.

During a discussion by a hospital class of the paucity of provisions for mental health in the community, a woman patient of about thirty-six, classified as dementia praecox, hebephrenic type, recalled that during the first world war she had attended a German parochial school in the United States. Her school work was of a very high grade and she had always received much commendation and marks of distinction from the nuns. Despite the fact that the use of the German language had been frowned upon by the public in general, one of the teachers, a nun, announced that the use of the German language would be continued in the school. Our patient said she did not agree with this, because she was, after all, an American. The nun had become quite wrought up over this "rebellion," and had evinced considerable hostility against our patient for sometime thereafter. Our patient related this with much feeling, speaking with great rapidity. She indicated that she had experienced a great emotional upset as a result and ended by saying she had never spoken of this episode to anybody before. It is evident that she was benefited from the catharsis activated by the general class discussion.

(c) *Intellectualization.* Group discussion aids the process of objectification of the patient's problems through which he can see them in a new perspective. Comments by patients and interpretation by the therapist increase insight. The patient comes to see the identity of his emotional problems with those of others, and as a result he feels less isolated. It is for this reason that Marsh [6] and Wender [7] consider one of the main functions of group psychotherapy to be the extroverting of the patient's mental energies. The role of the intellect in these functions should not be minimized. On this point Alexander [8] has stated: "Insight becomes deeper, more and more comprehensive, slowly enforcing its verdict, until the emotional patterns yield and its components are gradually forced into new, more satisfactory combinations. This process has no sharply limited termination. . . . On the other hand, after an insight has deeply penetrated— the patient cannot get rid of it any more—its voice is soft, its effect slow, but permanent."

One cannot deal long with mental patients without realizing to what extent their minds and lives, as well as those of the average person, are influenced by patterns of thought, or social images.[9] Hans Syz [10] remarks on the role of social images thus: "There is here, as . . . Burrow has found, a tendency to live up to an image of self, a state of constant transference to the exactions of this self-image as it is projected on the persons and institutions that compose the surroundings. The direct relation to immediate realities is lost and is replaced by an habitual mood-dependence upon reflected images. This arbitrary superstructure occasions anomalous tensions and artificial drives and these obstruct and contradict natural and unsophisticated action."

In a class of psychotic patients the observations are constantly made on the exactions of social images. An example of this is a male patient of about forty-five years of age, classified dementia praecox, paranoid type. He did not seem to be able to grasp the role of the mother as a cause of psychopathology whenever it was brought up for discussion in class. He staunchly defended the traditional constellation of ideas about the concept of motherhood. Later on when the subject of ambivalence was discussed

---

[6] Marsh: *loc. cit.*

[7] Wender, L.: Dynamics of Group Psychotherapy. *J. Nerv. Ment. Dis.*, July, 1936.

[8] Alexander, F.: The Voice of the Intellect is Soft. *Psa. Rev.*, January, 1941.

[9] Burrow, T.: Social Images versus Reality. *J. Abnorm. Psychol.*, Oct.–Dec., 1924.

[10] Syz, H.: Remarks on Group Anaylsis. *Am. J. Psychiat.*, July, 1928.

and illustrated with a case history, he appeared interested and agreed that there was much in what has been said. Still later, in an individual interview after he had left the hospital, he revealed how his mother had always dominated him. He alluded to the fact that he had become involved in a murder charge through her. The anamnesis corroborated his revelation and stated that the patient had driven his mother to the scene where she had shot and killed the woman to whom her husband was paying attention.

Most of his life this patient had been an unwilling subject of his mother's domination. His mother always made inordinate demands on him. With considerable feeling he recounted the impositions and strictures his mother had placed on his own domestic menage. At the time of his hospitalization he was separated from his wife and young son and was living with his mother. Now he was throwing off the maternal yoke. It was time, he said, that he pay more attention to the claims of his wife and child. This resolution the patient has kept, in the main, to his own satisfaction.

Within our limitations of space an exhaustive discussion of all reasonably well-known group psychodynamics would be impossible and we must proceed to the subject of Group Therapy techniques with psychotic patients.

(a) *Didactic or Pedagogical Group Psychotherapy.* By didactic or pedagogical group psychotherapy is meant Group Therapy administered through a textbook or prepared script.

In administering group psychotherapy in a large institution with the conditions prevalent in such, the present writer felt the desirability of certain provisions for the classwork. The same provisions will be found almost equally helpful in practice with private patients.

(1) Group psychotherapy should include a program of re-education and even academic education in the ordinary sense.

(2) It is desirable to have a comprehensive program which

can be taken over by another therapist as circumstances demand.

(3) A method of administration must be evolved that would provide a constant source of discussion and study, and prevent embarrassment to a new therapist as to choice of material.

(4) As far as possible a uniform standard of application needs to be provided.

Grotjahn,[11] in his experience with group psychotherapy (largely through lectures) in the armed forces, has observed the initial resistance at each session. There may be a tense interval before someone makes a "break" and begins the discussion. This resistance would obviously be reduced if the class pursued a systematic course of study.

Group psychotherapy as now practiced is most frequently administered and implemented by a series of lectures. It is evident that if they are to be comprehensive and informative they should follow each other in a systematic fashion and must therefore involve much preparation by the therapist. Group Therapy definitely must serve the purposes of re-education and even education in the academic sense. Even such thorough planning and preparation may not guarantee success. For many patients lectures can prove distasteful and disappointing. Inspirational lectures can arouse much enthusiasm and generate emotionally charged convictions, but under average conditions the audience or class remain passive listeners. It is only in so far as the lectures allude to material that touches off patients' identifications that the therapist can enlist active participation. It may not be entirely futile, therefore, to attempt to enlist systematic attention to the subject matter at hand. In pedagogical group psychotherapy this is more or less accomplished through the textbook from which the patients read aloud.[12]

Again, a lecturer may wonder what important points or nu-

[11] Grotjahn, M.: *Experiences with Group Psychotherapy in Cases of Veterans.* Paper Delivered at the One-Hundred-and-Second Annual Meeting of the American Psychiatric Association, Chicago, May 27th, 1946.

[12] A textbook for pedagogical group psychotherapy with patients is now in process of preparation by the writer.

ances he has failed to include in his talk, how forcefully he has made his point. Such doubts can be largely eliminated through pedagogical Group Therapy.[13]

Whether lecture or prepared script, the text serves in large part as the counterpart of interpretation as the latter is given in the individual psychoanalytic sessions. The text also serves as the sounding instrument that sets off in resonance the patients' recollections and affects. One need have little fear that the textbook would completely replace the therapist. The best textbooks ever written have not succeeded in displacing good teachers and, conversely, the most gifted teachers have found textbooks indispensable.

It is well known that a gifted teacher possesses something more than a knowledge of his subject; that he possesses certain qualities that make his teaching effective. It may be conceded that a good teacher is partly psychotherapist, and conversely, the good psychotherapist is something of a good pedagogue. Undoubtedly there is an area here in which some overlapping of skills and qualities exists.

The group psychiatrist is not primarily concerned with the amount of knowledge acquired by the psychotic patient, nor with how expeditiously it is acquired. No marks or grades are given. Rather, the psychiatrist is acutely sensitive to the reactions of his patients in the class and is attuned to the slightest nuances of speech and deportment. At the same time he is concerned with broadening the intellectual horizons of his patients and with placing intellectual tools at their disposal. Pedagogical Group Psychotherapy can be employed as the matrix of Group Therapy. It does not exclude other forms of Group Therapy such as psychodrama, for example, which can be given in conjunction with it.

"The considerations treated of in the above section led the writer to devise a mimeographed textbook called *Social Adjust-*

[13] The need for some systematization and simplification in the practice of psychotherapy in general has been well stated by Glover who has remarked: "In my view the advancement of psychotherapy requires the development of a psychotherapeutic technique demanding only the wisdom of an intelligent medical graduate and the morality of the Hippocratic oath he takes on graduation."

ment which was privately printed and used as a class textbook. The chapter titles of the book serve to suggest the character of the material dealt with. (1) Introduction; (2) Objectives of Classwork; (3) What Price Shame? (4) How it Began; (5) Reason and Impulse; (6) Mental Mechanisms; (7) The Natural or Biological Meaning of the Process of Thinking; (8) Mental and Personality Development; (9) Some Large-Scale Features of the Personality; (10) How We Think.

"So far as possible the therapist attempts to create an informal discussion group. Patients are free to ask questions at any time. Lively discussions are frequently begun in this manner. At the end of each chapter there is a list of review questions.

"In class each patient in turn reads a paragraph aloud and then summarizes it, recapitulates what he has read and comments on it as he chooses. He is not held strictly to account and the therapist will prompt him, amplify statements, or interpret obscure passages as encountered. If only one sentence has been read which has led to worthwhile discussion, catharsis, and objectification of the patient's difficulties, that period must be counted as very worthwhile, indeed.

"Group psychotherapy, as already implied, is not confined solely to the study of the textbook. Other books are frequently assigned to patients to report on. Written autobiographies are called for and occasionally submitted voluntarily. Symposia, debates, and various other activities are carried on as part of the therapy. For example, when dealing with the chapter on biology the class is taken for a tour of the clinical laboratory, shown the apparatus, and also slides of tissue cells and germs under the microscope.

"Despite subject matter which is probably quite involved for the average patient, it is significant how often 'complex indicators' are uncovered concerning which patients will evidence far more comprehension than they might otherwise be credited with. It is not necessary that the patient understand intellectually all the material dealt with in class; the processes of identification and group interaction contribute their own even more fundamental therapeutic effects. Also noteworthy is the fact that wherever the content of discussion engages the affective capacity, there the bar of language and the turn of phraseology appear to be a minimal hindrance to understanding." [14]

Classes should be held optimally three times a week. In an institution it can be more easily managed; in private practice one class a week may be found the most convenient. Class period is usually of one hour's duration.

(b) *Series of Lectures.* A system of lectures is probably the readiest means that comes to mind in the administration of group therapy with psychotics. When in 1918-19 Lazell [15] began a series of lectures to groups of patients he reported his results in the following terms: "Silent dreamy boys suddenly became interested and drank in every word, realizing that here was someone who understood their troubles."

Lectures can begin with a discussion of the reasons for admission to a hospital and of the relationship of society to mental patients. This subject is an extremely tender spot with practically all patients. Unopposed, the patient will rationalize an elaborate system of delusions concerning his commitment, but a series of objective, dispassionate explanations revivifies for him the objective world and recalls to him the objective criteria by which he, too, in his premorbid state, guided his existence. These lectures can be depended upon to evoke considerable comment, discussion, and catharsis.

The series of lectures may start with a discussion of mental illness and what is comprehended in the term. The lectures may then proceed to trace personality development and the way in which psychic dynamisms are employed by the patients. When these subjects are skillfully presented in simple language, many patients exhibit a surprising grasp of these psychological desiderata.

The following is a condensed outline of lectures to psychotic patients that may serve as a guide: [16]

[14] Quoted from *Group Psychotherapy; Theory and Practice*, by J. W. Klapman, *loc. cit.*, pp. 236-237.

[15] Lazell, E. W.: The Group Psychiatric Treatment of Dementia Praecox by Lectures in Mental Re-education. *U. S. Vet. Bur. Monthly Bull.*, September, 1930.

[16] Klapman, *ibid.*, pp. 204-234.

(c) *Case History Reading.* A device which seems quite unorthodox but which has been practiced by Schilder is that of reading the history of one of the patients in the class. Preferably the history should contain the psychodynamic relationships well worked out. At first glance this would appear the height of fatuity as the patient ordinarily would be regarded as the last person capable of grasping the significance of dynamic relationships. But this is not true, and Federn [17] has pointed out that as the psychosis loosens repressions, the patient is less resistive to receive such perceptions. Actual experience with the class method supports Federn's view. The writer has, on a number of occasions, read histories of patients in the class, not revealing their names, of course, as well as published case histories. The patients display great interest in these and may give unerring interpretations of the cases. Even a psychiatric article dealing with a fundamental problem is attentively followed by patients and abundantly commented upon. The writer recently read such an article by Tiebout [18] to a class from the *American Journal of Psychiatry* dealing with the rigid, omnipotent personality that underlies excessive drinking. The patients' intense interest, comments, and questions showed to what extent many of them felt personally involved. As unorthodox as this procedure may be, it resembles in some respects the psychoanalytic technique of giving an interpretation when the situation warrants it.

(d) *Autobiographies.* Schilder gave detailed directions to his small groups on the writing of their comprehensive biographies that were used in the group sessions. He worked with small groups of six to eight patients and closely adhered to psychoanalytic techniques. Such a method constitutes intensive group psychotherapy. It must also be remembered that Schilder exercised considerable selectivity in the choice of patients for particular groups. Under the usual conditions of a large mental hospital with large numbers of patients, practice of such intense psychoanalytic psychotherapy is less feasible.

(e) *Discussion.* As patients become assimilated into the therapeutic milieu, they begin to ask questions on almost all subjects alluded to in class. The therapist directs discussions; amplifies and interprets statements; makes addenda and corrections, and so supervises the discussions that they do not run too far afield. The questions patients direct to the therapist usually reflect the

[17] *loc. cit.*

[18] Tiebout, H.: Therapeutic Mechanisms of Alcoholics Anonymous. *Amer. J. Psychiat.,* January, 1944.

questioner's mental conflicts, and may be clues to the psychodynamic situation.

(f) *Symposia and Debates; Assignments.* Often the class will touch upon controversial subjects and such topics are best settled through a symposium or debate. Sides are chosen, and the contestants are supplied with references by the psychiatrist and assisted by the librarian and other members of the hospital staff or other patients. Sometimes patients report to the class on books or other topics that interest them. One patient gave a creditable talk on meteorology illustrated on the blackboard. Another took the subject of alchemy and prepared a thesis on the subject neatly typed and bound. He remained throughout his stay at the hospital an enthusiastic student of the subject and spent much time on research in the library after discharge from the institution.

The value of such activities and interests does not lie in the extension of knowledge, but rather in their extrovertive nature. They engender preoccupations outside of the patients' problems and foster better relationships and rapport with the institution's personnel and other patients. This is a great improvement over the regimen prevailing in ordinary mental hospitals where patients do little more than brood over fancied and real grievances or give themselves over to delusions and hostility against the hospital personnel. Under these circumstances patients regress and deteriorate.

(g) *Psychodrama.* Moreno,[19] viewing therapy as a dramatic technique, divides this treatment method into two phases: psychodrama on the spot, and psychodrama in the theater.

Psychodrama on the spot is a relatively less specific form of therapy. It consists of all contacts, associations, and everything that transpires between the patient and the personnel of the institution. Psychodrama on the stage is begun when the patient has been motivated adequately to desire to act out some aspect of his own personality, assisted by *auxiliary egos*, specially trained personnel of the institution to function in this capacity. Psychodrama is acted out spontaneously in a specially con-

[19] Moreno, J. L.: The Group Approach in Psychodrama. *Sociometry*, May, 1942.

structed theater with three superimposed platforms or stages. Moreno refers to it as the *spontaneity theater*. During the course of the psychodrama the patient-spectators as well as the patient-actors are apt to be activated and take part in spontaneous play, and thus the whole group participates in the therapy, either on the stage or as spectators.

Solomon [20] has attempted a modification of the practice of psychodrama in that after the psychodynamics of a given case have been studied and understood a dramatic script is written and acted out.

It is rather difficult to evaluate the results of Group Psychotherapy objectively, since an accurate statistical evaluation would have to be made first of spontaneous improvements and recoveries that occur in mental hospitals without any type of planned therapy. At present electric shock or insulin therapy is employed coordinately with Group Psychotherapy, and it is difficult to determine the part each plays in the recovery of patients. Objective tests before and after treatment would under these circumstances be inconclusive. A large number of patients, including those receiving shock therapy, tested with the Bell Adjustment Inventory showed marked improvement after about three months of Group Therapy. At present an attempt is being made to give mass Rorschachs at intervals.

In estimating results of Group Psychotherapy a thumbnail sketch of an individual case may prove of some value.

A young woman, a mental defective, not of very low grade, had a speech difficulty in addition to poor reading ability and could hardly be understood when she attempted to read aloud. The psychiatrist suggested to her that she practice reading aloud. After some weeks there was a distinct improvement in her enunciation and reading ability. Through questioning one of her ward-mates, the therapist learned that she had dutifully carried out instructions and had frequently read aloud to other patients.

[20] Solomon, A. P.: *A Critical Study of Analytically Oriented Group Psychotherapy Utilizing Psychodynamics*. Paper Delivered at the One-Hundred-and Second Annual Meeting of the American Psychiatric Association, Chicago, May 30, 1946.

She was complimented in class on her diligence. When she was about to leave the hospital, she spoke to the therapist about a WPA evening school that she expected to attend. About two years later, in 1943, when she came to visit the institution, she encountered the therapist on the grounds. She informed him, among other things, and with pardonable pride, that she had graduated from the aforementioned school and had received a certificate. She was working and earning her own living; liked her work, and was getting along well in all her relations.

Discouraged, and resigned to the fate that her disability seemed to impose, she would have remained a helpless charge on the community, sinking ever deeper into a slough of indifference and despondency, had not her class attendance served to strike a spark of initiative through which she had been enabled to utilize her scanty native capacities.

(1) Group Psychotherapy is a means of bringing about positive transferences of patients to the therapist and to each other. Because of this, emotional acceptance of interpretations by the therapist are facilitated to a degree practically inconceivable to one accustomed to the perfunctory relationship between doctor and patient as they occur in the ward of a mental institution conducted on traditional lines.

(2) Patients receive a measure of emotional catharsis, and their problems are subjected to a process of intellectualization and objectification. Thus tensions that arise from social imagery can be appreciably lessened.

(3) Group Psychotherapy lends itself to a didactic or pedagogical approach (which forms the material of this chapter).

(4) There is room for the belief that group treatment is more effective in areas that are relatively inaccessible to individual psychotherapy with psychotics. It would appear that correction of deficiencies in social attitudes are better corrected in a social setting than in individual treatment in the case of psychotics.

(5) For those who have used the group method both in private practice and hospital wards, the value of Didactic Group Psychotherapy is convincing and evident, but as yet no method has been devised for objective evaluation of its effectiveness.

Chapter Thirteen

PLAN AND FANTASY IN GROUP THERAPY

"Plan" and *"fantasy"* are two products of the human mind which have a number of peculiarities in common and differ mainly in one respect. They are both created by means of imagination and both represent the fulfillment of certain of our wishes. They differ with regard to the degree to which facts and surmises are used in their composition. The mental picture of the fulfillment of a wish is called a plan when it is composed of knowable facts that can be used as guides in all the activities that lead to the materialization of the plan. It is called a fantasy when surmises or conjectures are used in its composition to such a degree that they cannot be used as guides in actualization of the wish. Sometimes a fantasy is modified into a plan; in fact, most plans start out as fantasies, which are gradually transformed by the elimination of surmises and the substitution of facts in their stead. Some fantasies are so far removed from reality that their transformation into a plan is impossible as distinguished from those that are reality-syntonic and therefore realizable.

In thinking about the future, planning and fantasying often go hand in hand; the fantasy—not confined entirely to knowable facts—extends much farther than does a plan. Even anxious anticipation of the future permits comparison with plan and fantasy. This wishful thinking utilizes the engrams of past experiences to build expectation, which may not at first find conscious acceptance. The same is also true of the dream.

In evaluating something new that promises to expand in time

to come and to bring in its wake freedom from suffering, it is well to keep in mind these three forms of wishfulfillment: plan, fantasy and dream. Almost every day confronts us with examples of planning that never goes beyond the present: with fantasying that substitutes surmises for facts: with dreaming that creates apprehension, where apprehension is not justified. And the examples are particularly numerous in the field of therapy.

To the great majority of people Group Therapy is still a new concept and practice, and already we see its potentialities being used in the three different manners, sketchily indicated above: careful examination and planned application by a few, exaggerated expectation of its helpfulness by many, and apprehension of disastrous effects by very many.

The term "Group Therapy" itself indicates the assumption that the group experience, i.e., the contacts and relationships of the individual members of the group with one another, is the therapeutic factor in this form of treatment. In the foregoing chapters the reader has been able to learn that various forms of relationships are possible in groups. As two extremes we can mention the activity group (mostly used with children) in which the individual members are allowed to act out with a very large degree of freedom their impulses, desires and wishes in mutual contact; and the group of adults where a subject of interest to all the members is discussed with as much freedom as the inhibitions and anxieties of the participants permit. The intensity and the nature of the contact between the members of the group are entirely different in each: direct and usually more or less violent in the former, indirect and restrained in the latter.

One can formulate the difference in yet another way by stating that the members of activity groups have yet to learn the experience of belonging together, of being parts of a whole; whereas the members of the other types of groups have learned this lesson to a certain extent, but not in the areas of conflict in their private lives.

In the earlier chapters it has been made clear that the group therapist fulfills a very important role in the process of adjustment which is made possible or accelerated by the group experience. It was also repeatedly stated that satisfactory results in adjustment can be, and are being, achieved if certain conditions regarding the choice of the members of the groups and the training of the group therapists are complied with. The question must even have arisen in the mind of the reader whether in certain cases therapeutic results could not be obtained in a shorter span of time by Group Therapy than by treatment of the individual alone.

These then are a few of the more important facts about Group Therapy. Taking these facts into account our plans will move in the direction of continued investigation and research with regard to such problems as: Who is apt to profit by Group Therapy? Who is apt to profit more by Group Therapy than by individual therapy? What determines the type of Group Therapy a specific individual needs most? Are variations of the present types of Group Therapy possible? Which requirements are essential in the training of the group therapists? In fact, these problems are constantly being subjected to study and experiment. New and better formulations are continually being evolved which in turn lead to fresh problems.

But it is inevitable that the imagination of those who are interested in this form of therapy should go beyond the limitations of known facts and that it should build images of what may be realized ten or twenty years hence. These people cannot but create fantasies of what now seems desirable, but may very soon prove feasible. The "planners" like to believe (and why not?) that with a greater knowledge of what constitutes aptitude for Group Therapy it will be possible to treat a great many more people for all sorts of psychiatric disorders than can be achieved by individual therapy. The objection that Group Therapy never brings about the same *deep* changes that certain forms of individual psychotherapy do, is easily refuted by the fact that we often find permanent improvement and even cure achieved also by less deep individual therapy. Besides, our therapeutic methods change with social and economic conditions and what may not yet be possible now may be very well possible ten or twenty years hence.

If we are going to apply Group Therapy in an increasing measure it will be necessary to find or create the conditions under which its application can be most easily introduced. It is one of my own fantasies that some of the precepts evolved by Group Therapy should be incorporated into the teaching methods in the classroom and in the ways of dealing with children's fundamental needs in the school. Most schools have provisions that take into account the assets of individual pupils. There are the ungraded, the normal and the rapid advance classes. Many schools have a psychological and a counselling service. To create facilities for individual psychotherapy in the school seems at present like an impossible task, but it would be possible to create facilities to apply some of the practices and principles evolved by group therapists in both forms, activity and discussion, for children with special personality difficulties who do not fit into the ordinary school routine. Every one of the types of groups for children and adolescents about whom I have learned in child guidance work could be formed in the type of school we envisage for the future. Instead of having to refer these children to clinics and agencies, the schools can learn to deal with them in their own set-up, especially where psychiatric advice would be readily available. Truly a fantasy! How far is our school system of today still removed from the insights which made the birth and growth of Group Therapy possible!

The case of the schools represents but one instance of the possibilities for preventing or removing disturbances in organized masses by the application of Group Therapy to individuals who, through illness or personality disorder, cause disturbance wherever numbers of people are brought together or organized temporarily or permanently.[1]

As almost all forms of therapy, Group Therapy will in the future make its contributions to the prevention of disorders, in addition to its usefulness as a method of treatment. Even at this relatively

[1] This idea was already expressed in a paper on the so-called war-neuroses read on October 18, 1942 during the Postgraduate Fortnight of the Academy of Medicine, in which a specific type of occupational group treatment was advocated.

early stage of its development it has taught us a great deal about the dynamics involved in the relationship between the group therapist and the members of his group. Varying in its tactics according to the type of group (activity, discussion, mixed, collective effort, and so on) and to the class of members of the groups (developmental level, special interests, and so forth) it has one basic quality, namely, to provide the members of the group with the fullest psychological opportunity for a new start in the effort for better adjustment. It requires a great deal of understanding and experience to grasp this basic principle in its origin and in its implications. It is my expectation—or fantasy, if you wish—that the application of this principle to the collective efforts of even those groups of people who have acquired a normal degree of adjustability, will greatly increase effectiveness by eliminating the inner friction caused by misunderstood rivalry, competition and resentment which, as remnants of the past, always threaten to vitiate the opportunities of the future.

INDEX

A

Abreaction, 24
Acting out, 152, 154
Activities, immobilizing, 128
Activity and interview groups, relation of, 261
Activity Group Therapy, 31 et seq., 76, 132
  aims of, 32
  and schizoid personality, 84
  effects of, 33, 34, 57
  group therapist in, 33
  in treatment of neuroses, 38
  values for exceptional child, 63
  with exceptional children, 62, 64, 65
Activity, libido-binding, 108
Advice, in Group Therapy, 162
Aggression, in treatment of neuroses, 136
Alexander, F., 156, 249
Allee, A. C., 25
Allergy and psychological factors, 156
American Group Therapy Association, 15
Analyst, as symbol, 153
Animals, the social life of, 25
Anxiety, and neuroses, 136
  and speech symptom, 179
  in Group Therapy, 9, 154
Anxiety states and Interview Group Therapy, 99
Aphonia, hysterical, 181
Assignments in Didactic Group Therapy, 257
Attitude towards self, in neuroses, 127
Autobiographies, in Didactic Group Therapy, 256

B

Balance of impulse and its control, 19
Baruch, Dorothy W., 158, 159, 163
Behavior disorder, 43
Bernstein, C., 156
Biological growth and dynamic processes, 20
Blanket techniques vs. individualization, 23
Brooklyn Child Guidance Center, 220
Burrow, Trigand, 25, 249
Burt, Cyril, 72

C

Case history recording in Didactic Group Therapy, 255, 256
Cases
  Allergy
    F/1, 175
    F/2, 174
    F/9, 169-171
    M/4, 164
    M/11, 171-174
  Character deviation
    Arnold, 84-86
    Herman, 76-84
    Pearl, 86-91
    Rhea, 91-94
  Dementia praecox, hebephrenic type
    woman, 248
  Dementia praecox, paranoid type
    man, 249-250
  Exceptional children
    Jack, 69-70